101 SONGS FOR EASY GUITAR BOOK 4

Wise Publications
London/New York/Sydney

Music Sales Limited
8/9 Frith Street, London W1V 5TZ, England
Music Sales Pty. Limited
120, Rothschild Avenue, Rosebery, NSW 2018, Australia

This book © Copyright 1981 by
Wise Publications
ISBN 0.86001.933-0
Order No. AM 29075

Compilation & Design: Pearce Marchbank and Peter Evans

Music Sales complete catalogue lists thousands
of titles and is free from your local music
book shop, or direct from Music Sales Limited.
Please send a cheque or postal order for £1.50 for postage to
Music Sales Limited, 8/9 Frith Street, London W1V 5TZ.

Printed in England by
Dotesios Ltd., Trowbridge, Wiltshire

Black Magic Woman
Words and Music: Peter Green

Moderate Rock

1. Got a black mag - ic wom - an. __ Got a black mag - ic
   - by. __ Don't turn your back on me

wom - an. __ I've got a black mag - ic wom - an.
ba - by. __ Don't turn your back on me ba - by,

Got me so blind I can't see, that she's a
stop mess - in' 'round with your tricks. Don't turn your

black mag - ic wom - an, she's tryin' to make a dev - il out of me.
back on me ba - by, you just might pick up __ my mag - ic sticks.

1. 2.

3.

2. Turn your back on me ba -   4. Got your spell on me ba - by.
3. (Instrumental)

You got your spell on — me ba-by. —   Yes, — you got your

spell   on me ba-by,   turn-in' my heart in-to   stone.   I

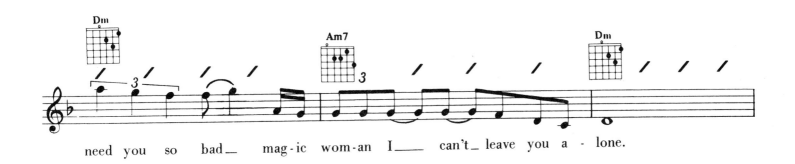

need you so bad—   mag-ic wom-an I—   can't— leave you a - lone.

(Instrumental)

My Generation

Words and Music: Pete Townshend

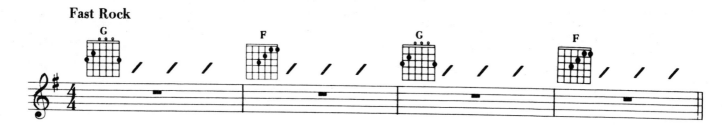

Fast Rock

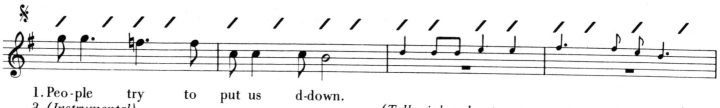

1. Peo-ple try to put us d-down. (Talk-in' a-bout my gen - er - a - tion.)
3. (Instrumental)

Just be-cause we get a - round._ (Talk - in' a-bout my gen - er - a - tion.)

Things they do look aw - ful c - c - cold. (Talk - in' a - bout my gen - er - a - tion.) I

hope I die__ be - fore I get old._ My gen - er - a
(Talk - in' a-bout my gen - er - a-tion.)

To Coda

tion, this is my__ gen - er - a - tion, ba - by.

2. Why don't you all f - fade a - way, *(Talk - in' a - bout my gen - er - a - tion.)* and

don't try and dig what we all s - say. *(Talk - in' a - bout my gen - er - a - tion.)* I'm

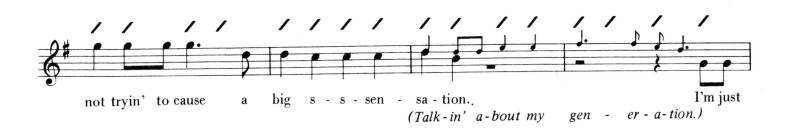

not tryin' to cause a big s - s - sen - sa - tion.. *(Talk - in' a - bout my gen - er - a - tion.)* I'm just

talk - in' a - bout my g - g - g - gen - er - a - tion. *(Talk - in' a - bout my gen - er - a - tion.)* My gen - er - a -

D. S. 𝄋 *(repeat verses) al Coda*

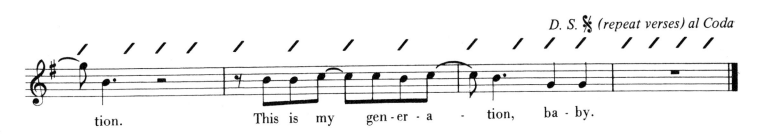

tion. This is my gen - er - a - tion, ba - by.

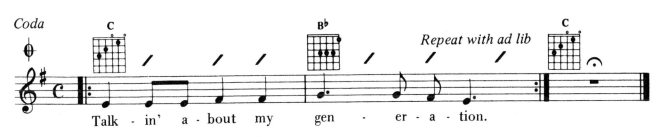

Coda

C   **B♭**   *Repeat with ad lib*   **C**

Talk - in' a - bout my gen - er - a - tion.

NOTE: Repeat verse 2 in the key of A; verse 1 in B ; verse 2 in C; before Coda.

Green Onions

Music: Booker T. Jones, Steve Cropper, Al Jackson Jr., Lewie Steinberg

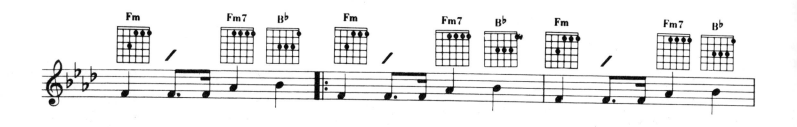

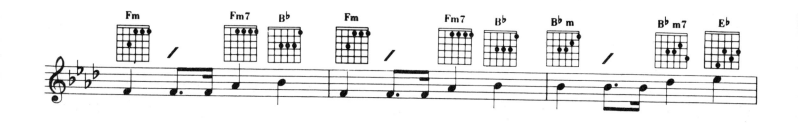

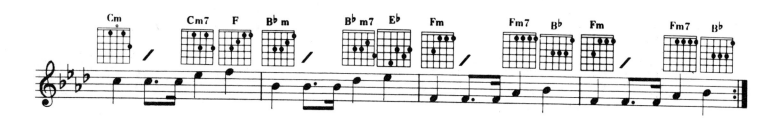

Rapture

Words: Deborah Harry
Music: Chris Stein

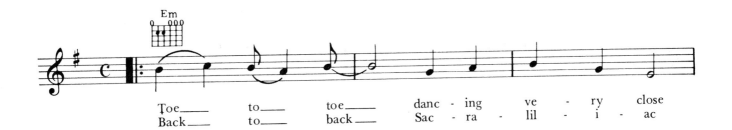

Toe__ to__ toe__ danc-ing ve - ry close
Back__ to__ back __ Sac - ra - lil - i - ac

Bo - dy breath - ing _____ al - most com - a - tose __
Spine - less move - ment _____ and a wild at - tack __

Wall __ to __ wall, __ peo - ple hyp - not - ised _____
Face __ to __ face __ sight - less sol - it - ude ____

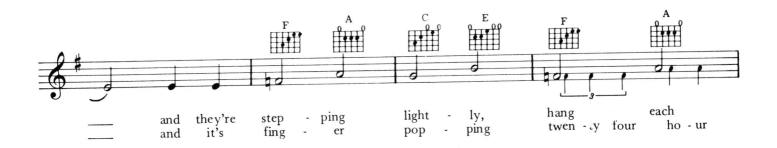

__ and they're step - ping light - ly, hang each
__ and it's fing - er pop - ping twen - ty four ho - ur

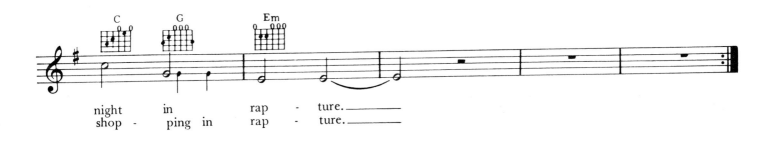

night in rap - ture.
shop - ping in rap - ture.

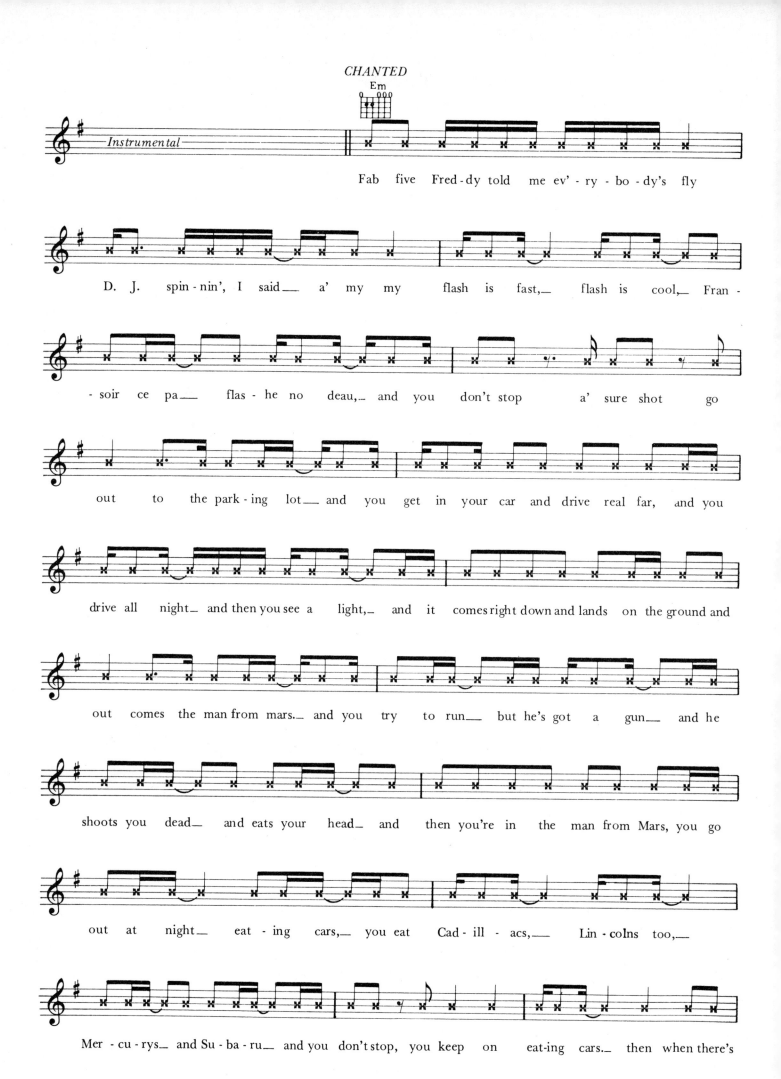

CHANTED

Em

Instrumental

Fab five Fred-dy told me ev'-ry-bo-dy's fly

D. J. spin-nin', I said___ a' my my flash is fast,___ flash is cool, Fran-

-soir ce pa___ flas-he no deau,___ and you don't stop a' sure shot go

out to the park-ing lot___ and you get in your car and drive real far, and you

drive all night___ and then you see a light,___ and it comes right down and lands on the ground and

out comes the man from mars.___ and you try to run___ but he's got a gun___ and he

shoots you dead___ and eats your head___ and then you're in the man from Mars, you go

out at night___ eat-ing cars,___ you eat Cad-ill-acs,___ Lin-colns too,___

Mer-cu-rys___ and Su-ba-ru___ and you don't stop, you keep on eat-ing cars.___ then when there's

no more cars_ you go out at night_ and eat up bars_ where the peo - ple meet_

face to face,_ dance cheek to cheek,_ one to one,_ man to man,_ Dance

Em

Toe to toe_ don't move too slow_ 'cause the man from mars is through with cars,_ he's
Now you see_ what you wan - na be__ just have your par - ty on T. V._'cause the

eat - in' bars,_ yeah, wall to wall, _ door to door,_ hall to hall_ he's gon-na
man from Mars,_ won't eat up bars,_where the T. V.'s on and now he's gone_ back

eat 'em all,_ rap - ture be pure, take a tour_
up to space,_ where he won't have to has-sle with the human race, and you hip hop, and you

through the sewer_ don't strain your brain_ paint a train,_ you'll be sing - ing
don't stop, just blast off a sure shot, 'cause the man from Mars stopped

in the rain,_ ba-by don't stop do Punk Rock
eat - in' cars_ and eatin' bars, and now he on - ly eats gui - tars,_ get down!

1

Instrumental

2

To Fade

Instrumental

Well

Angels On The Balcony

Words by Laura Davis
Music by Jimmy Destri

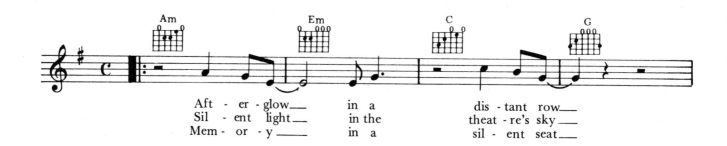

After - glow____ in a   dis - tant row____
Sil - ent light____ in the   theat - re's sky____
Mem - or - y ____ in a   sil - ent seat____

the door__ is op - en and__ the   lights are cold.____
phan - tom cig - ar - ette__ and a   sil - ent cry____
   mel-o - dy____ on__ a   long re - treat____

the child - ren come__ in here__ and they   dare the ghost____
the door__ is op - en and__ it's   cold out - side____
like__ an ang - el on__ a   bal - co - ny____

like a fi - re burn - ing   in a stone____
run and hide____   run and hide____
like an ang - el on__ a   bal - co - ny____

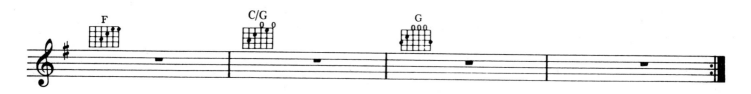

To Coda ⊕

They can still see him sing - ing on the corn -

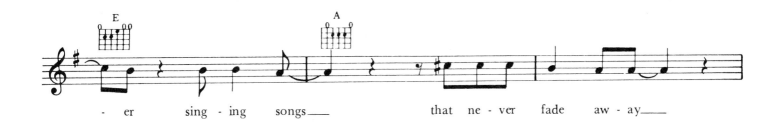

- er sing - ing songs___ that ne - ver fade aw - ay___

fade in - to the kids ___ that come a - long___

D.C. al Coda   ⊕ CODA   To Fade

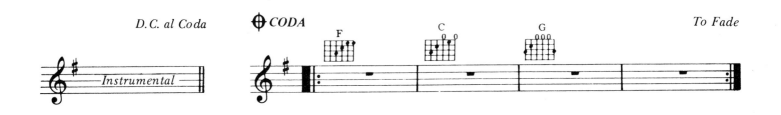

Instrumental

Do The Dark

Words and Music: Jimmy Destri

There   you   are_____   giv - ing   can -
Walk   on   glass_____   with   the   mas -

- dy   mak - ing   con - fi - dence   with   an   eas -
- ter   there's   no   ques - tion   he   can't   ans -

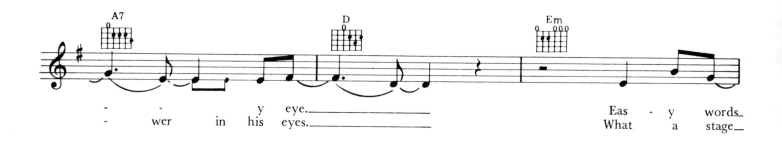

- wer   in   his   eyes._____   Eas - y   words____
- y   eye._____   What   a   stage____

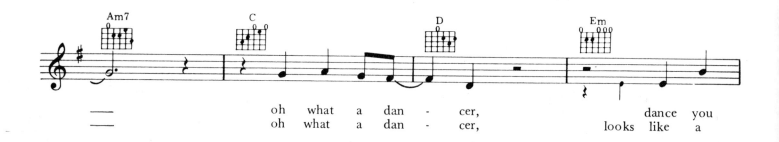

_____   oh   what   a   dan - cer,   dance   you
_____   oh   what   a   dan - cer,   looks   like   a

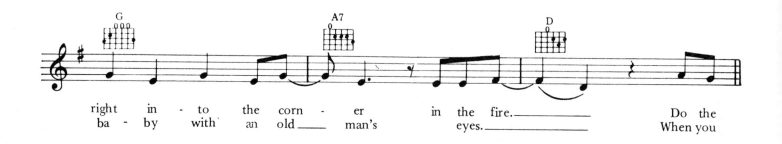

right   in - to   the   corn - er   in   the   fire._____   Do   the
ba - by   with   an   old_____   man's   eyes._____   When   you

dark ap - os - tle   do the side - walk hus - tle,   do the in -
break the rules___   and you burn your brid - ges,   and your

- vi - si - ble dance___   in the fi - re, fi - re,   fi - re, fi - re.___
fin - gers itch and they're get-ting wet___ when you look at her___

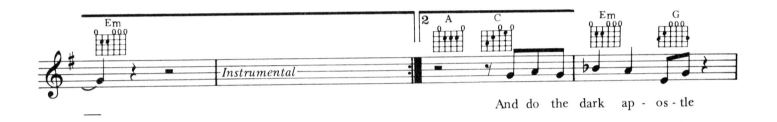

Instrumental

And do the dark ap - os - tle

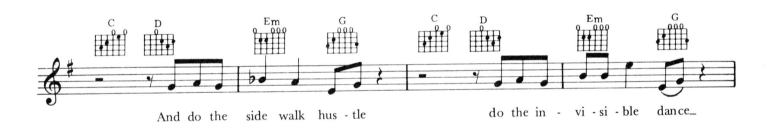

And do the side walk hus - tle   do the in - vi - si - ble dance___

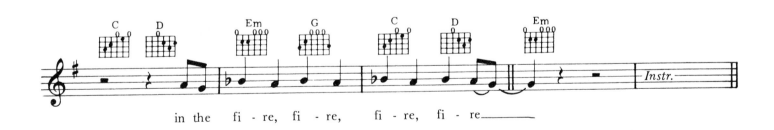

in the fi - re, fi - re,   fi - re, fi - re_____   *Instr.*

To Fade

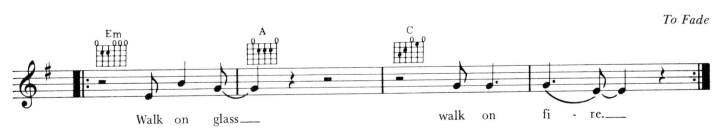

Walk on glass___   walk on fi - re.___

15

T-Birds

Words: Deborah Harry
Music: Nigel Harrison

Cir - cle high,   cir - cle   low___   jam-mers fly   on the dot   timed
On the dot   in the,   in the   slot___   on the dot   timed
Coil it up, wind it   out, strike it   hot   coil it up plummed

T - Birds___   you show you show   whip - lash   go___
kiss - es___   in the slot,   on the   dot,   tie the knot,
ser - pent.___   coil it up, wind it   out,   strike it hot,

you show, you show   T - Birds___
in the slot,   no   miss - es___
coil it up my   T - Bird_(ser - pent   curl___

My T - Birds___   T - Birds,
My T - Birds___   T - Birds,
___)   My T - Birds_____   T - Birds,
                                   (Rule the   world_____

My my T - Birds.___
My my T - Birds.___
My my T - Birds.___
___)

Heart Of Stone

Words and Music: Mick Jagger & Keith Richards

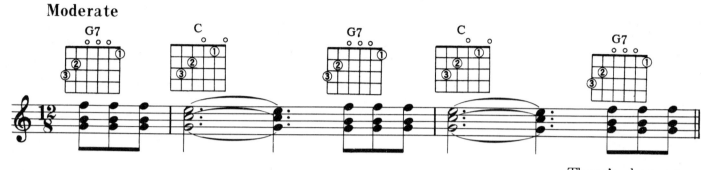

There've been so

ma - ny___ girls that I've known,
look-ing___ that same old way,

I've made so man - y cry,
If you try act-ing sad,

And still I won-der why.
You'll on-ly make me glad.

Here comes the lit - tle girl,
Better lis-ten lit - tle girl,

I see her walk-ing down the street,
You go on walk-ing down the street,

She's all by her-self,
I ain't got no love,

Try-ing so hard to please,
I ain't the kind to meet,

But— she'll
But— you'll

F

nev-er break, nev-er break, nev-er break, nev-er break

this heart of

Am

2nd time To Coda

C

G7

stone, oh no no, this heart of stone.___

What's dif-f'rent a-

C

F

bout___ her?

I don't real-ly know.

D7

G

No mat-ter how I try

I just can't make her cry.

But__ she'll

nev-er break, nev-er break, nev-er break, nev - er break this heart of

stone, oh no no no this heart of stone.__ Don't keep on

Coda

stone._____ You'll nev-er break this heart of stone._____

20

Sittin' On A Fence

Words and Music: Mick Jagger & Keith Richards

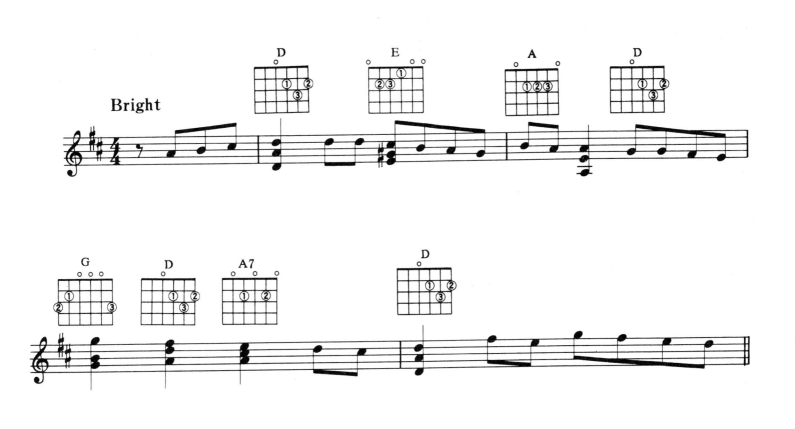

Bright

Since I was young I've been ver-y hard__ to please,

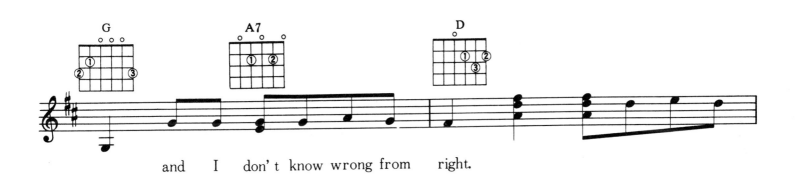

and I don't know wrong from right.

But there is one thing I will nev-er un-der-stand;

some of___ the sick things that a girl___ does to a man, so

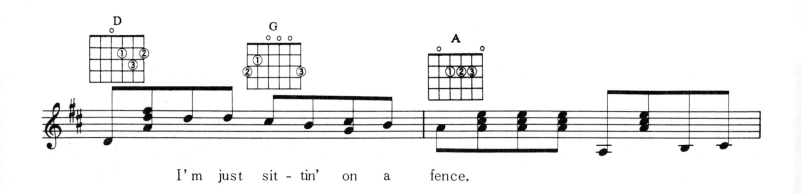

I'm just sit-tin' on a fence.

You can't say I got no sense.

Try - in' to make up my mind;— real - ly is too hard a bind.—

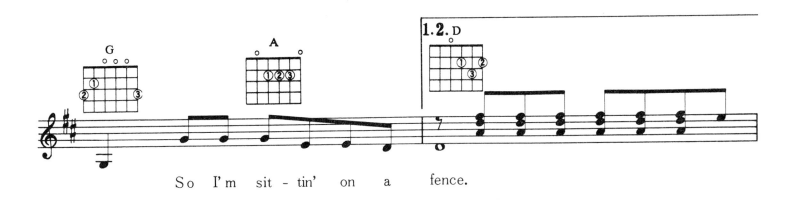

So I'm sit - tin' on a fence.

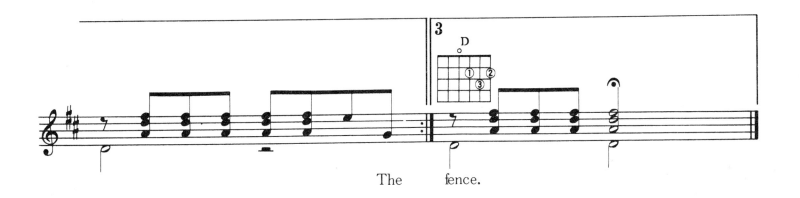

The fence.

2. All of my friends at school grew up and settled down;
   And they mortgaged up their lives.
   One thing's not said too much but I think it's true.
   They just get married 'cos they've nothing else to do, (To Chorus)

3. The day can come when you get old and sick and tired of life;
   You just never realize.
   Maybe the choice you made wasn't really right;
   But you go out and you don't come back at night.

No Expectations

Words and Music: Mick Jagger & Keith Richards

Slowly

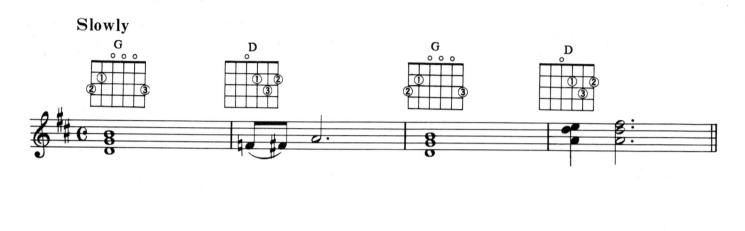

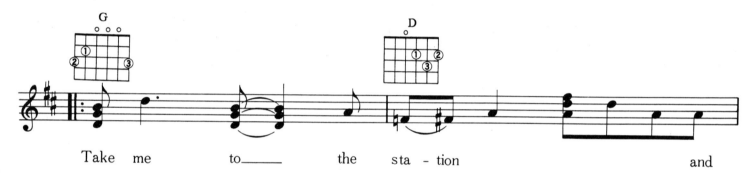

Take me to___ the sta - tion   and

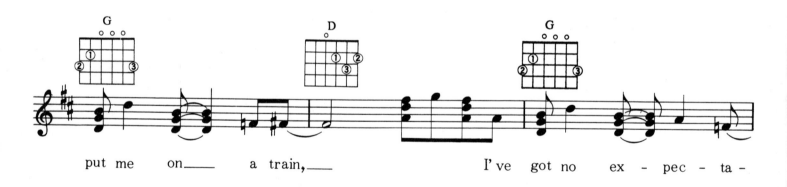

put me on___ a train,___   I've got no ex - pec - ta -

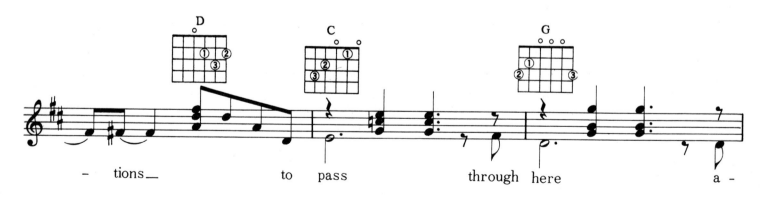

- tions___   to pass   through here   a -

gain._____

2. Once I was a rich man and now I am so poor,
    But never in my sweet, short life have I felt like this before.

3. Your heart is like a diamond, You throw your pearls at swine,
    and as I watched you leaving me you packed my peace of mind.

4. Our love was like the water that splashes on a stone,
    Our love is like our music, it's here and then it's gone.

5. So take me to the airport and put me on a plane.
    I've got no expectaions to pass through here again.

It's All Over Now

Words and Music: B & S Womack

Medium Rock

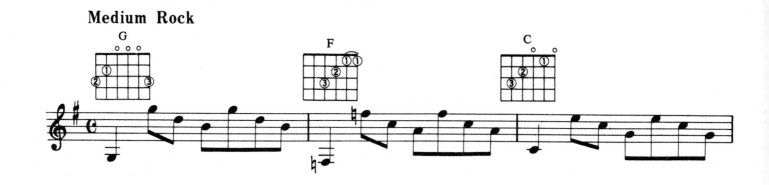

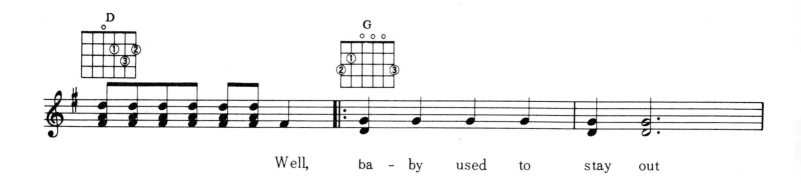

Well, ba - by used to stay out

all night long._____ She made me cry;____

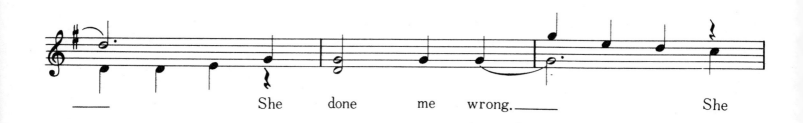

____ She done me wrong.____ She

hurt my eyes_____ o - pen,   that's no   lie; _____

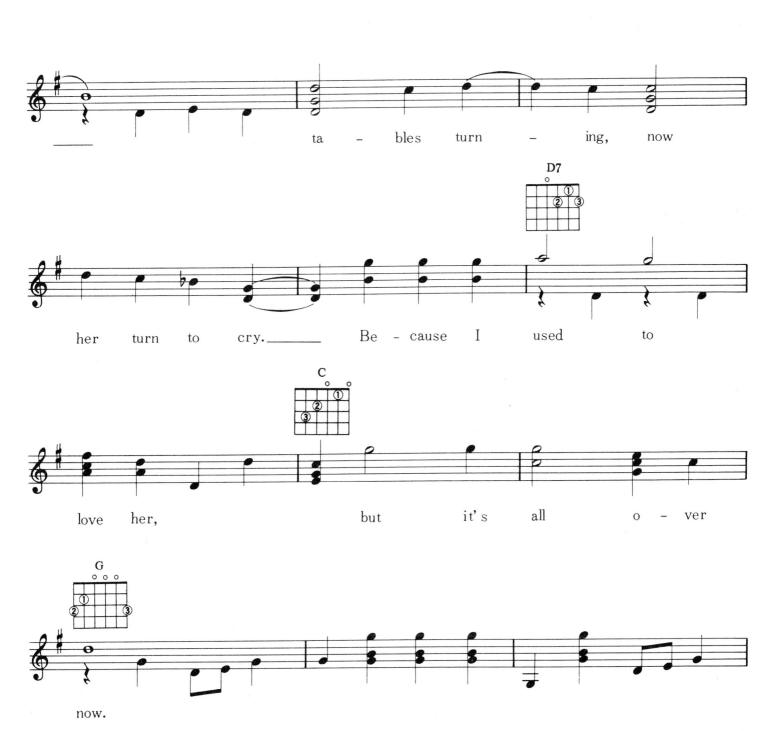

_____   ta - bles turn - ing, now

D7

her turn to cry._____   Be - cause I   used   to

C

love her,   but   it's   all   o - ver

G

now.

Well,   she   Well,   I

Be - cause I   used   to   love   her,

but   it's   all   o - ver   now.

Repeat and fade

2. Well, she used to run around with ev'ry man in town.
   Spent all my money playing a high-class game.
   She put me out; it was a pity how I cried;
   The tables turning now, her turn to cry.

3. Well, I **used** to wake the morning, get my breakfast in bed.
   When I gotten worried she could ease my aching head.
   But now she's here and there with ev'ry man in town,
   Instead of trying to take me for that same old clown.

Good Times, Bad Times

Words and Music: Mick Jagger & Keith Richard

There've been good times   There've been bad

times.   I've had   my share___   of hard times___   too.___

___   But I lost my___ faith in the world_____

hon - ey, when I____ lost you._____

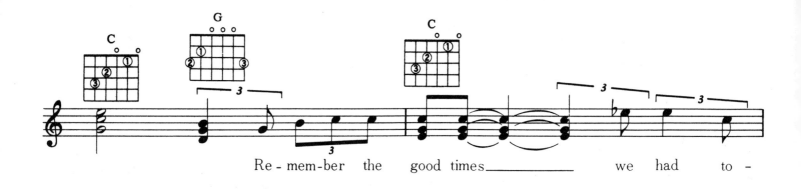

Re - mem - ber the good times_____ we had to -

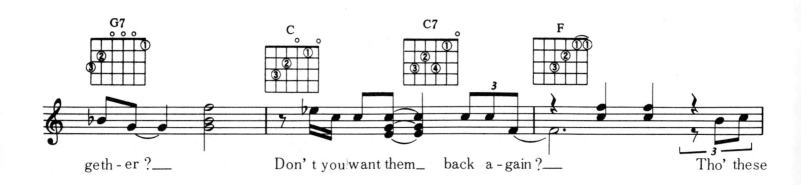

geth - er ?__ Don't you want them_ back a - gain ?__ Tho' these

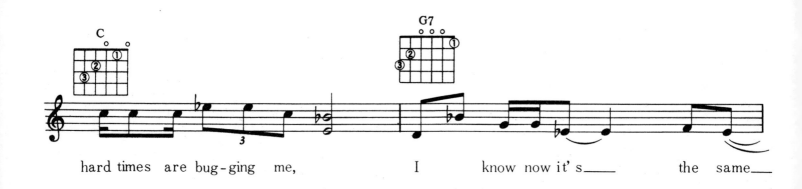

hard times are bug - ging me, I know now it's____ the same__

There's got-ta-be trust in this world,

or it won't____ get ver-y far.____ Well,

trust-ing some-one,____ or just gon – na be war.____

(Hum)_____ etc.____

I'm Free

Words and Music: Pete Townshend

Moderate

I'm free to do what I want__ __ an-y old__ time.__ __ I'm time.__ Love me, __

hold me,___ love me,___ hold me,___ I'm

free an-y old___ time to get what I want._____

I'm free to sing my song___ tho' it is___

1. out of tune._____ 2. I'm time._____

Coda free to do what I want___ an-y old___ time.___

Lady Jane

Words and Music: Mick Jagger & Keith Richards

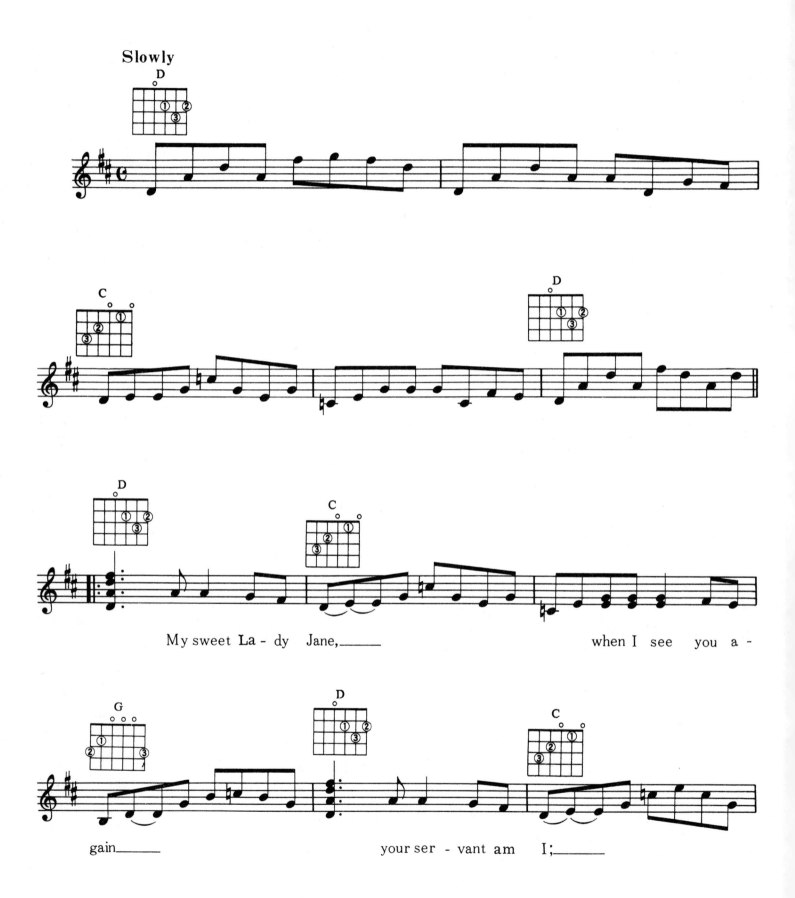

Slowly

My sweet La - dy Jane,_____ when I see you a-

gain_____ your ser - vant am I;_____

and will hum - bly re - main._____

Just   be   dis - pleased,   my love,   On   bend - ed

knee   my love,   I   pledge   my - self   to   La - dy

Jane._____

2. My dear Lady Anne, I've done what I can.
    I must take my leave; for promised I am.
    The play is run, my love.
    Your time has come my love.
    I pledge my soul to Lady Jane.

3. Oh, my sweet Marie, I wait at your cue.
    When sands have run out; for your lady and me.
    When love is nigh, my love.
    Her station's right my love.
    Life is secure with Lady Jane.

Daytime Friends

Words and Music: Ben Peters

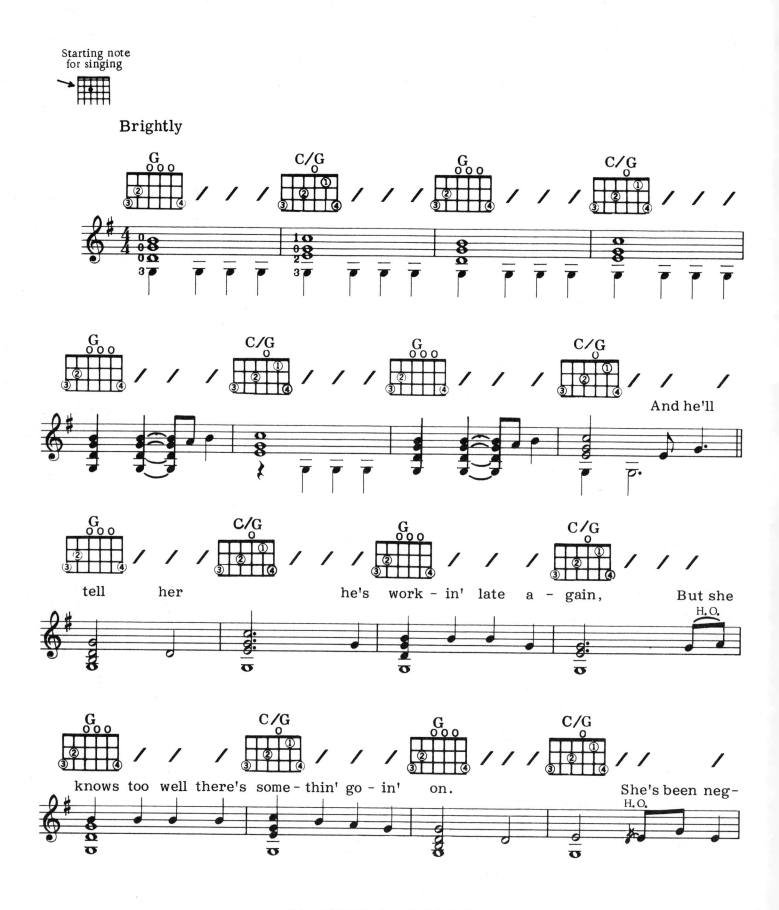

Chorus

38

To Coda ⊕

hands in the light of day.

But when it's o — ver, there's no
won — ders why some

peace of ____ mind, Just a long — ing for the
men nev — er find That a wom — an needs a

1. C/G

way things should have been.____ And she
lov — er and a friend.____

2. G

Day-time
D.S. al Coda 𝄌

Coda

(hold) (hold) (hold)

She Believes In Me

Words and Music: Steve Gibb

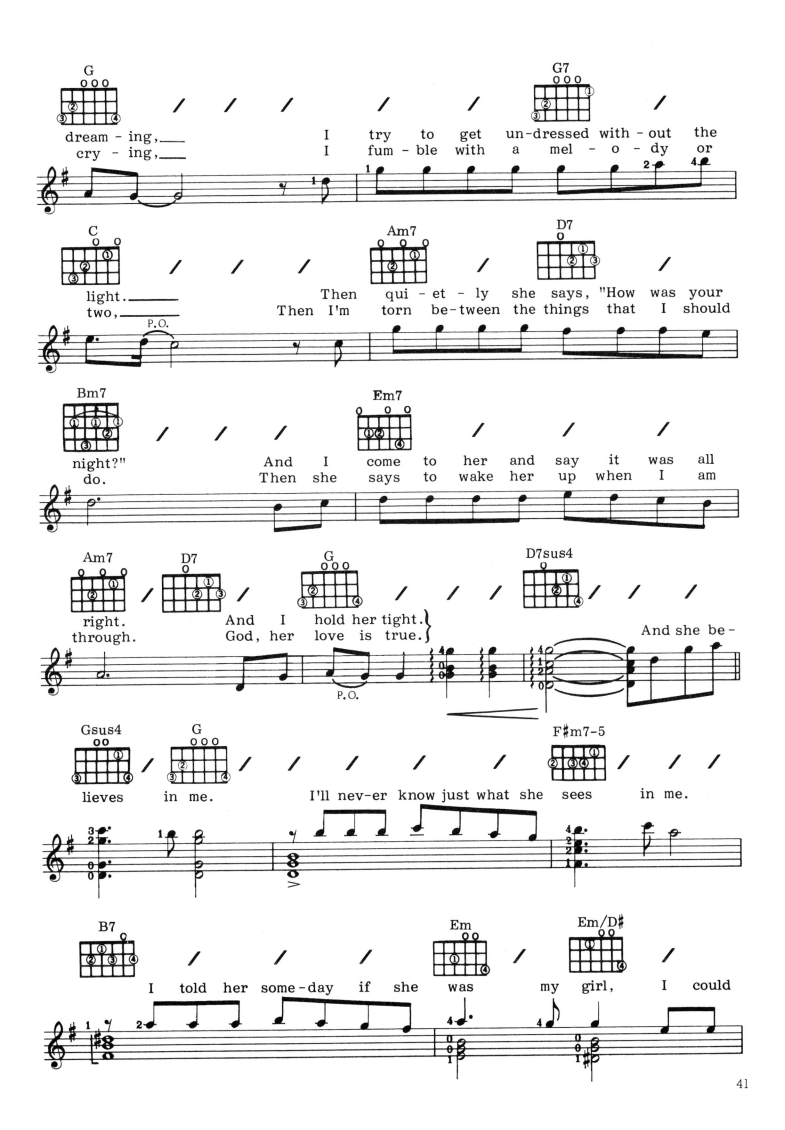

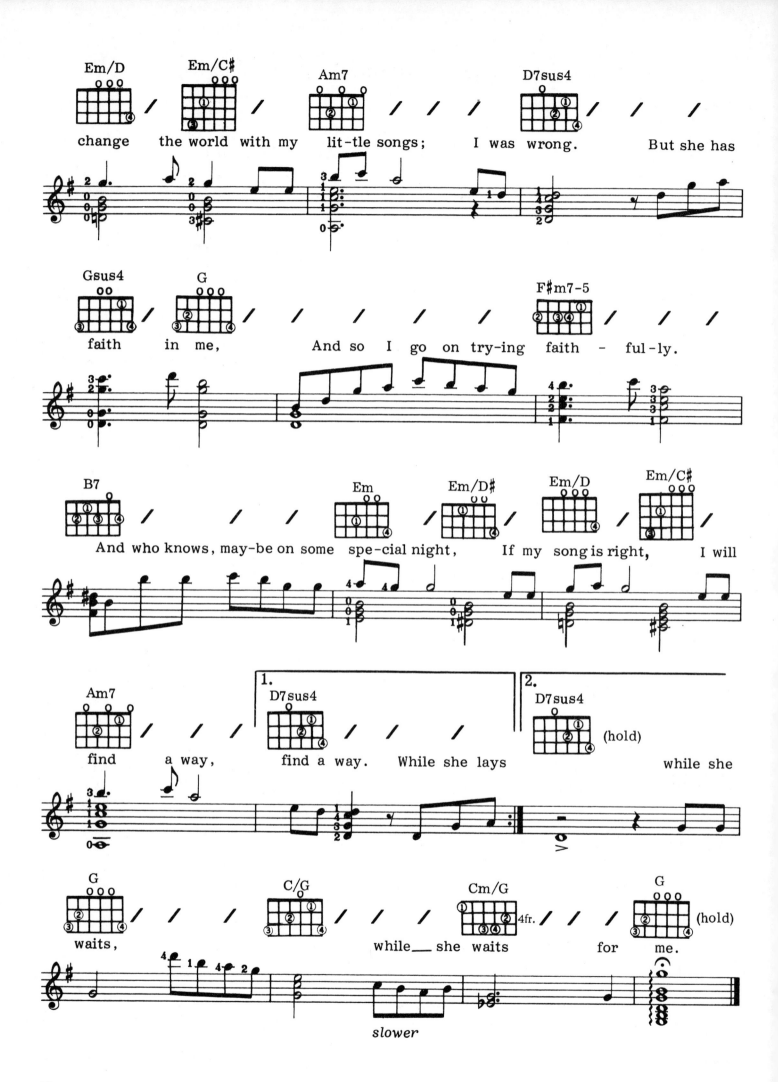

It Takes A Lot To Laugh, It Takes A Train To Cry

Words and Music: Bob Dylan

Well, I ride on the mail-train babe, __ can't buy a thrill. __

Well I've been up all night, __ lean-in' on the win-dow sill. __

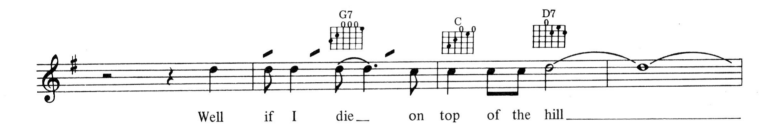

Well if I die __ on top of the hill __

__ well if I don't make it __ you know my ba - by will. __

2. Don't the moon look good, mama,
Shinin' through the trees?
Don't the brakeman look good, mama,
Flagging down the "Double Es"?
Don't the sun look good
Goin' down over the sea?
Don't my gal look fine
When she's comin' after me?

3. Now the winter time is coming,
The windows are filled with frost.
I went to tell everybody,
But I could not get it acrost.
Well I wanna be your lover, baby,
I don't wanna be your boss,
Don't say I never warned you
When your train gets lost.

Like A Rolling Stone
Words and Music: Bob Dylan

ev - 'ry - bo - dy that was   hang - in' out___   now you

don't   talk   so   loud_____   now   you   don't

seem   so   proud_____   a - bout   hav - ing   to   be   scroung - ing

for   your   next   meal. _____   How does   it

feel   how   does   it   feel,

to   be   with - out   a   home,

like   a   com - plete   un - known,

45

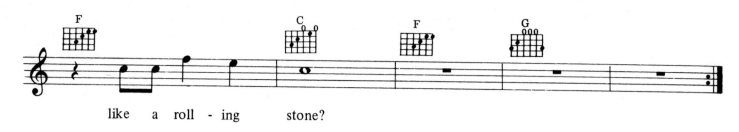

like   a   roll - ing   stone?

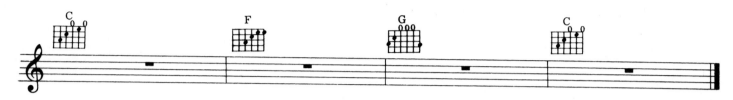

Verse 2   You've gone to the finest school all right, Miss Lonely
But you know you only used to get
Juiced in it.
And nobody's ever taught you how to live on the street
And now you're gonna have to get
Used to it.
You said you'd never compromise
With the mystery tramp, but now you realise
He's not selling any alibis,
As you stare into the vacuum of his eyes
And ask him do you want to
Make a deal?
        Chorus.

Verse 3   You never turned around to see the frowns on the jugglers and the clowns
When they all come down
And did tricks for you
You never understood that it ain't no good
You shouldn't let other people
Get your kicks for you.
You used to ride on the chrome horse with your diplomat
Who carried on his shoulder a Siamese cat,
Ain't it hard when you discovered that
He really wasn't where it's at,
After he took from you everything
He could steal.
        Chorus.

Verse 4   Princess on the steeple
And all the pretty people're drinkin', thinkin'
That they got it made.
Exchanging all kinds of precious gifts and things
But you'd better lift your diamond ring,
You'd better pawn it babe,
You used to be so amused
At Napoleon in rags and the language that he used
Go to him now, he calls you, you can't refuse
When you got nothing, you got nothing to lose,
You're invisible now, you got no secrets
To conceal.
        Chorus.

When The Ship Comes In

Words and Music: Bob Dylan

Masters Of War

Words and Music: Bob Dylan

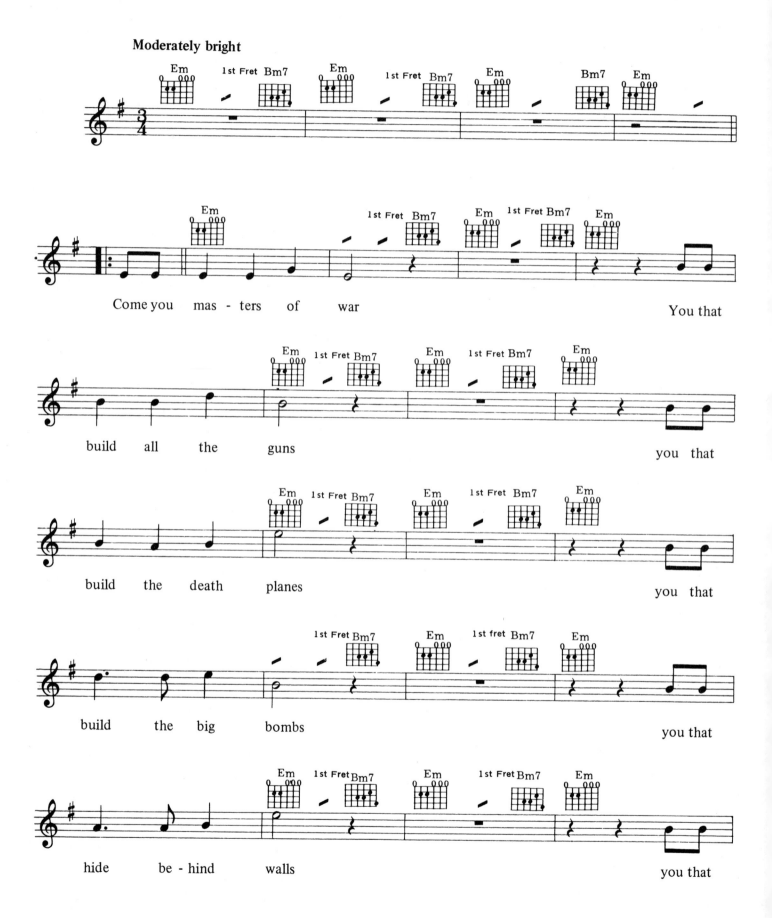

Moderately bright

Come you mas - ters of war   You that

build all the guns   you that

build the death planes   you that

build the big bombs   you that

hide be - hind walls   you that

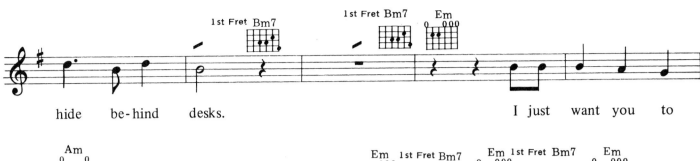

hide be-hind desks.   I just want you to

know I can see through your masks.

Verse 2   You that never done nothin'
            But build to destroy
            You play with my world
            Like it's your little toy
            You put a gun in my hand
            And you hide from my eyes
            And you turn and run farther
            When the fast bullets fly.

Verse 3   Like Judas of old
            You lie and deceive
            A world war can be won
            You want me to believe
            But I see through your eyes
            And I see through your brain
            Like I see through the water
            That runs down my drain.

Verse 4   You fasten the triggers
            For the others to fire
            Then you set back and watch
            When the death count gets higher
            You hide in your mansion
            As young people's blood
            Flows out of their bodies
            And is buried in the mud.

Verse 5   You've thrown the worst fear
            That can ever be hurled
            Fear to bring children
            Into the world
            For threatenin' my baby
            Unborn and unnamed
            You ain't worth the blood
            That runs in your veins.

Verse 6   How much do I know
            To talk out of turn
            You might say that I'm young
            You might say I'm unlearned
            But there's one thing I know
            Though I'm younger than you
            Even Jesus would never
            Forgive what you do.

Verse 7   Let me ask you one question
            Is your money that good
            Will it buy you forgiveness
            Do you think that it could
            I think you will find
            When your death takes its toll
            All the money you made
            Will never buy back your soul.

Verse 8   And I hope that you die
            And your death'll come soon
            I will follow your casket
            On a pale afternoon
            And I'll watch while you're lowered
            Down to your death bed
            And I'll stand o'er your grave
            Till I'm sure that you're dead.

Positively 4th Street

Words and Music: Bob Dylan

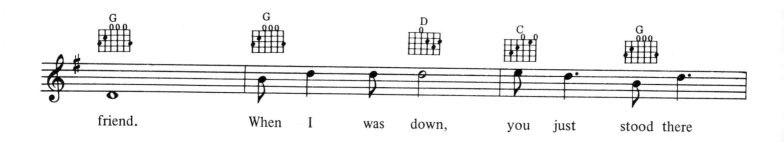

You got a lot-ta nerve__ to say you are my

friend. When I was down, you just stood there

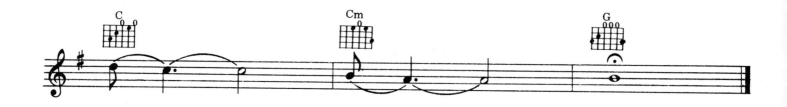

grin - ning.____

2. You got a lotta nerve
   To say you gotta helping hand to lend
   You just want to be on
   The side that's winning.

3. You say I let you down
   You know it's not like that
   If you're so hurt
   Why then don't you show it.

4. You say you lost your faith
   But that's not where it's at
   You had no faith to lose
   And you know it.

5. I know the reason
   That you talk behind my back
   I used to be among the crowd
   You're in with.

6. Do you take me for such a fool
   To think I'd make contact
   With the one who tries to hide
   When he don't know to begin with.

7. You see me on the street
   You always act surprised
   You say "how are you?", "good luck",
   But you don't mean it.

8. When you know as well as me
   You'd rather see me paralyzed
   Why don't you just come out once
   And scream it.

9. No I do not feel that good
   When I see the heart breaks you embrace
   If I was a master thief
   Perhaps I'd rob them.

10. And now I know you're dissatisfied
    With your position and your place
    Don't you understand
    It's not my problem.

11. I wish that for just one time
    You could stand inside my shoes
    And just for that one moment
    I could be you.

12. Yes I wish that for just one time
    You could stand inside my shoes
    You'd know what a drag it is
    To see you.

Eagle

Words and Music: Benny Andersson & Bjorn Ulvaeus

Moderately (with a lilt)

They came fly - in' from far - a - way,   now I'm un - der their
As all good friends we talk all night   and we fly wing to

spell.   I love hear - ing the sto - ries that they_____
wing.   I have ques - tions and they know ev - 'ry -

—— tell.   They've seen plac - es be -
thing.   There's no lim - it to

yond my land   and they've found new ho - ri - zons.
what I feel,   we climb high - er and high - er.

They speak strange - ly but I un - der - stand___
Am I dream - in' or is it all_____ real,___

___ and I dream I'm an ea - gle,
___ is it true I'm an ea - gle,

and I dream I can spread my wings.
is it true I can spread my wings?   Fly - in'

high, high, I'm a bird in the sky,___ I'm an

ea - gle that rides___ on the breeze.___

High, high, what a feel - ing to fly_____ o - ver

moun - tains and for - ests and seas _____ and to

go an - y - where _____ that I please. _____

And I dream I'm an

Knowing Me, Knowing You

Words and Music: Benny Andersson, Stig Anderson & Bjorn Ulvaeus

1. No   more ___   care - free ___   laugh - ter ___
2. Mem - 'ries, ___   good   days, ___   bad   days ___

si - lence ___   ev - er ___
they'll   be ___   with   me ___

af - ter. ___   Walk - ing through an emp - ty house ___
al - ways ___   in ___   these old fa - mil - iar rooms ___

tears in my eyes. ___
chil - dren would play, ___

This is where the sto-ry ends,___ this is good-bye.___
and there's on-ly emp-ti-ness___ noth-ing to say. ___

Chorus

Know-ing me, know-ing

you there is noth-ing we can do.___ Know-ing me, know-ing

you, we just have to face it this time,___

___ we're through. Break-in' up is nev-er

ea-sy I know, but I have to go. Know-ing

Take A Chance On Me

Words and Music: Benny Andersson and Bjorn Ulvaeus

59

when the pret - ty birds ___ have flown, Hon - ey, I'm still free, __

__ take a chance on me. __ Gon - na do my ver -

y best and it ain't no lie, __ If you put me to __

__ the test, if you let me try, __ take a

chance on me. _____ take a

chance on me. _____ 2. Oh, you can

Gm

We can go____ danc - ing, We can go____ walk - ing as
take your time,____ ba - by, I'm in no____ hur - ry, I

F

long as we're____ to - geth - er;
know I'm gon - na get____ you;

Gm

Lis - ten to____ some mu - sic, may - be just ____ talk - ing, you'd
You don't wan - na hurt ____ me, ba - by, don't ____ wor - ry,

F

get to know____ me bet - ter. 'Cause you know I got
I ain't gon - na let____ you. Let me tell you now

Dm   Bb

so much that I wan - na do, ____ when I dream I'm a - lone with you, ____ it's
my love is ____ strong e - nough ____ to ____ last when ____ thing's are rough, ____ it's

61

mag - ic._____ You want me to leave it there,_
mag - ic._____ You say that I waste my time,_

a - fraid of a love af - fair,_ but I think you know_
but I can't get it off my mind,_ No, I can't let go ____

that I can't let go. ____
'cause I love you so. ____

If you change your mind _____   } I'm the first in line,_
If you change your mind _____   }

__ Hon - ey, I'm still free, ___ take a chance on me._

__ If you need me let __ me know gon - na be a - round._

Repeat and fade

If you got no place ___ to go when you're feel - ing down. ___ If you're all a - lone ___ when the pret - ty birds ___ have flown, Hon - ey, I'm still free, ___ take a chance on me. ___ Gon - na do my ver - y best, ba - by, can't you see, ___ got - ta put me to ___ the test, take a chance on me. ___ If you change your mind ___

Honey, Honey

Words and Music: Benny Andersson, Stig Anderson and Bjorn Ulvaeus

1. Hon - ey, hon - ey, how __ you thrill __ me, a - ha, hon - ey, hon - ey.
2. Hon - ey, hon - ey, let __ me feel __ it, a - ha, hon - ey, hon - ey.
3. Hon - ey, hon - ey, touch __ me ba - by, a - ha, hon - ey, hon - ey.

Hon - ey, hon - ey, near - ly kill __ me, a -
Hon - ey, hon - ey, don't __ con - ceal __ it, a -
Hon - ey, hon - ey, hold __ me ba - by, a -

ha, hon - ey, hon - ey.   I'd   heard a - bout you __ be - fore. ___
ha, hon - ey, hon - ey.   The   way that you kiss __ good - night. ___
ha, hon - ey, hon - ey.   You   look like a mo - vie star. ___

___   I   want - ed to know __ some more. ___   And
___   The way that you hold __ me tight. ___   I
___   But I know just who __ you are. ___   And

now I know what ___ they mean, _____ you're a love ma - chine. ___
feel like I wan - na sing _____ when you do your thing. ___
hon - ey, to say ___ the least, _____ you're a dog - gone beast. ___

Oh, you make me diz - zy.   (3rd verse Instrumental) ___   I

don't wan - na hurt ___ you ba - by,   I   don't wan - na see ___ you cry. ___

So   stay on the ground ___ girl, you bet - ter not get too high. ___

But   I'm gon - na stick   to   you _____ boy,   you'll
(Instr.) _____

nev - er get rid of me. _____   There's no oth - er place ___ in this

world where I ra - ther would be. ___

Back In Black

Words and Music: Angus Young, Malcolm Young, Brian Johnson

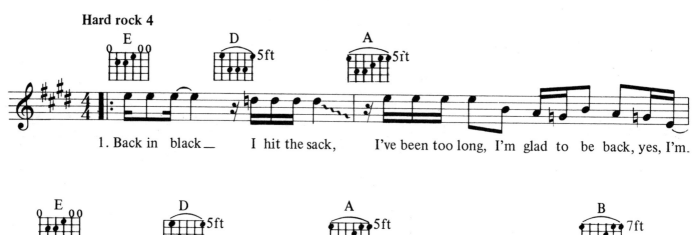

1. Back in black __ I hit the sack, I've been too long, I'm glad to be back, yes, I'm.

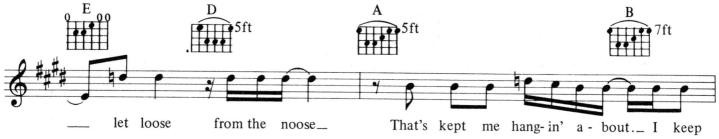

__ let loose from the noose __ That's kept me hang-in' a-bout. __ I keep

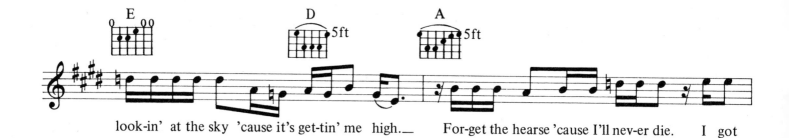

look-in' at the sky 'cause it's get-tin' me high. __ For-get the hearse 'cause I'll nev-er die. I got

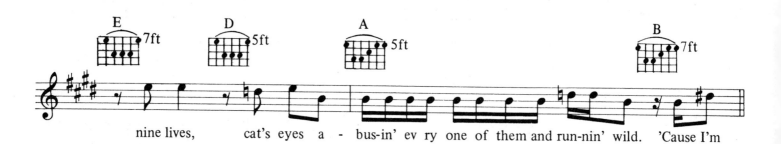

nine lives, cat's eyes a - bus-in' ev ry one of them and run-nin' wild. 'Cause I'm

CHORUS

back, yes I'm back __ Well I'm back, yes I'm

back,   Well I'm   back,_____   back._____ Well I'm

To Coda ✛

back in black,__   yes, I'm   back in__ black.__   back in__ black__ well I'm

✛ CODA

No Chord

back   in__   black.__

(guitar)

Well I'm   back_____

2. Back in the back of a Cadillac
   Number one with a bullet, I'm a power pack.
   Yes, I'm in a bang with the gang,
   They gotta catch me if they want me to hang.
   'Cause I'm back on the track, and I'm beatin' the flack
   Nobody's gonna get me on another rap.
   So, look at me now, I'm just makin' my play
   Don't try to push your luck, just get outta my way.

   Chorus

   Guitar Solo

   Chorus

   Guitar Solo

   Chorus

You Shook Me All Night Long

Words and Music: Angus Young, Malcolm Young, Brian Johnson.

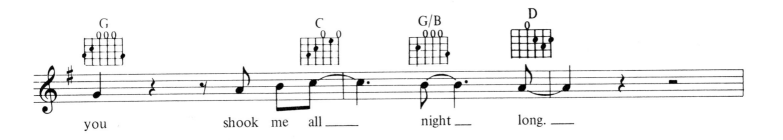

you   shook me all ____ night __ long. __

To Coda ⊕

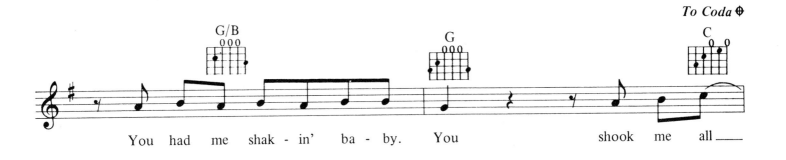

You had me shak - in' ba - by.   You   shook me all ____

D.%. (no repeats) al Coda

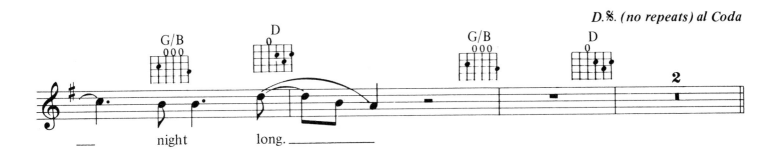

__ night   long. _____

⊕ *CODA*

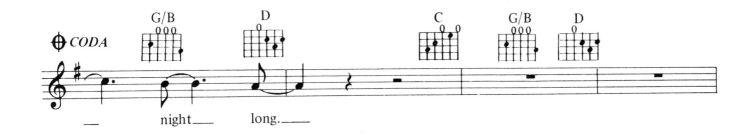

__ night __ long. __

Yeah, you shook _ me   all ____ night   long.

Have A Drink On Me

Words and Music: Angus Young, Malcolm Young, Brian Johnson

Rock And Roll Ain't Noise Pollution

Words and Music: Angus Young, Malcolm Young, Brian Johnson.

Spoken: Hey, there, all you middle men. Throw away your fancy clothes. And while you're out there sittin' on a fence, so get off your ass and come down here, 'cause Rock 'N' Roll ain't no riddle man. To me it makes good, good sense.

1. Hea-vy de-ci-bels are play-in' on my gui-tar.__ We got vi-bra-tions com-in' up from the floor.__ Well, just lis-'nin' to the rock that's giv-in' too much__ noise.__ Are you deaf, you wan-na hear some__ more.__ We're just talk-in' a-bout the fu-ture,__ For-get a-bout the past.__ It'll

2. I took a look inside your bedroom door
   You looked so good lyin' on your bed.
   Well, I asked you if you wanted any rhythm and love
   You said you wanna rock 'n' roll instead.
   We're just talkin' about the future
   Forget about the past
   It'll always be with us
   It's never gonna die, never gonna die.

   Chorus

   Guitar Solo

   Chorus

Wasted Time

Words and Music: Don Henley & Glenn Frey

Slowly, in 2

Well, baby, there you stand
You're back out on the street.

with your lit - tle head down in your
And you're try - in' to re -

hand. Oh, my God, you can't be - lieve it's
mem - ber. How do you start it o - ver? You

hap - pen - ing a - gain. Your ba - by's gone and you're
don't know if you can. You don't care much for a

all a - lone, and it looks like the end.
stran - ger's touch, but you can't hold your man.

So you live _____ from day to day,

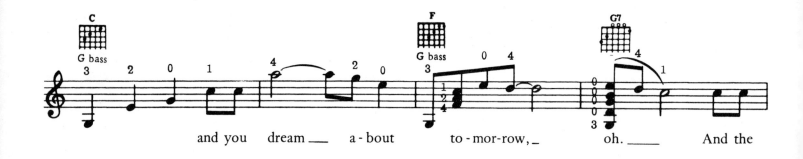

and you dream ___ a-bout to-mor-row, _ oh. _____ And the

hours go by like min - utes, ___ and the shad-ows come _ to stay. _____
mem - ber what you told ___ me ___ be-fore you went out on ___ your own: _____

_____ So ya take a lit - tle some-thin' to
_____ "Some-times to keep it to-geth - er we got to

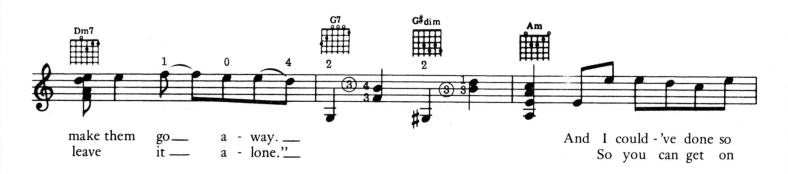

make them go ___ a - way. ___ And I could - 've done so
leave it ___ a - lone." So you can get on

After The Thrill Is Gone

Words and Music: Don Henley & Glenn Frey

Bridge

1. What can you do____ when your dreams come true____ and it's
not quite like __ you __ planned? What have you done__ to be
los - ing the one?__ You held it so tight__ in your hand. all.

Coda

af - ter the thrill__ is gone.

Additional lyrics

Verse 3.   Time passes and you must move on.
            Half the distance takes you twice as long.
            So you keep on singing for the sake of the song
            After the thrill is gone,
            After the thrill is gone.

Bridge 2.   You're afraid you might fall out of fashion,
            And you're feeling cold and small.
            Any kind of love without passion,
            That ain't no kind of loving at all.

Verse 4.   Same dances in the same old shoes;
            You get too careful with the steps you choose.
            You don't care about winning, but you don't want to lose
            After the thrill is gone,
            After the thrill is gone.

The Wreck Of The Edmund Fitzgerald

Words and Music: Gordon Lightfoot

Moderately slow, in 1

1. The leg - end lives on from the Chip - pe - wa on down of the big lake they called "Git - che Gu - mee." The lake, it is said, nev - er gives up her dead when the skies of No - vem - ber turn gloom - y. With a load of iron ore twen - ty - six thou - sand tons more than the Ed - mund Fitz - ger - ald weighed emp - ty,

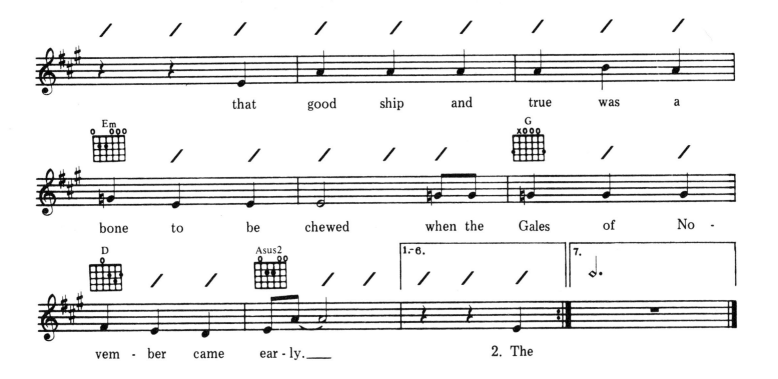

that good ship and true was a

bone to be chewed when the Gales of No -

vem - ber came ear - ly.____   2. The

2. The ship was the pride of the American side coming back from some mill in Wisconsin.
   As the big freighters go it was bigger than most with a crew and good captain well seasoned,
   Concluding some terms with a couple of steel firms when they left fully loaded for Cleveland.
   And later that night when the ship's bell rang, could it be the north wind they'd been feelin'?

3. The wind in the wires made a tattletale sound and a wave broke over the railing.
   And every man knew as the captain did too 'twas the witch of November come stealin'.
   The dawn came late and the breakfast had to wait when the Gales of November came slashin'.
   When afternoon came it was freezin' rain in the face of a hurricane west wind.

4. When suppertime came the old cook came on deck sayin', "Fellas, it's too rough t' feed ya."
   At seven P.M. a main hatchway caved in; he said, "Fellas, it's bin good t' know ya'."
   The captain wired in he had water comin' in and the good ship and crew was in peril.
   And later that night when 'is lights went outta sight came the wreck of the Edmund Fitzgerald.

5. Does anyone know where the love of God goes when the waves turn the minutes to hours.
   The searchers all say they'd have made Whitefish Bay if they'd put fifteen more miles behind 'er.
   They might have split up or they might have capsized; they may have broke deep and took water.
   And all that remains is the faces and the names of the wives and the sons and the daughters.

6. Lake Huron rolls, Superior swings in the rooms of her ice-water mansion.
   Old Michigan steams like a young man's dreams; the islands and bays are for sportsmen.
   And farther below Lake Ontario takes in what Lake Erie can send her,
   And the iron boats go as the mariners all know with the Gales of November remembered.

7. In a musty old hall in Detroit they prayed, in the "Maritime Sailors' Cathedral."
   The church bell chimed 'til it rang twenty-nine times for each man on the Edmund Fitzgerald.
   The legend lives on from the Chippewa on down of the big lake they called "Gitche Gumee."
   "Superior," they said, "never gives up her dead when the Gales of November come early!"

Did She Mention My Name

Words and Music: Gordon Lightfoot

Moderate Country tempo

It's so nice to meet __ an old friend and pass the time __ of day, and talk a - bout __ the home - town a mil - lion miles __ a - way. Is the ice still in the riv - er? Are the old folks still the same? And by the way, _____ did she men - tion __ my name? Did she men - tion my name just in

rain do you re - mem - ber if she dropped a name or two?

_____ Won't you say hel - lo __ from

some - one? There'll be no need to ex - plain. __ And by the

way, _____ did she men - tion my __

name? _____

Is the landlord still a loser? Do his signs hang in the hall?
Are the young girls still as pretty in the city in the fall?
Does the laughter on their faces still put the sun to shame?
And by the way, did she mention my name?
Did she mention my name just in passing?
And when the talk ran high did the look in her eye seem far away?
Is the old roof still leaking when the late snow turns to rain?
And by the way, did she mention my name?

There But For Fortune

Words and Music: Phil Ochs

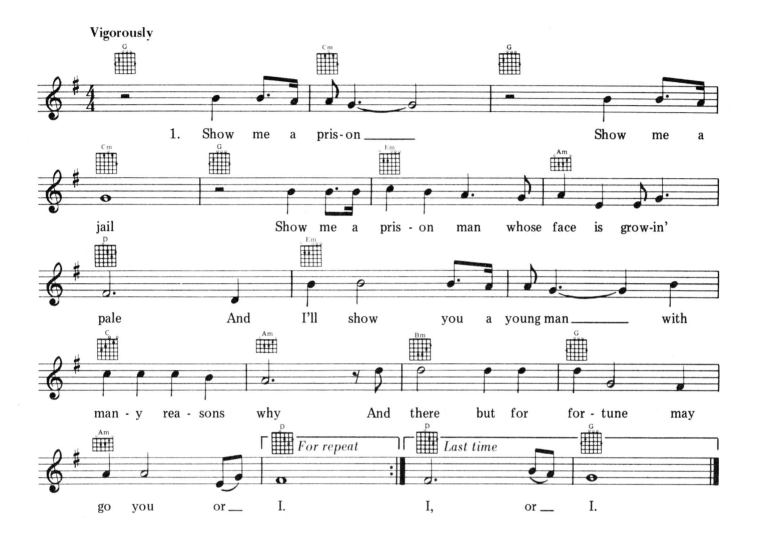

2. Show me an alley, show me a train,
   Show me a hobo who sleeps out in the rain,
   And I'll show you a young man with many reasons why,
   And there but for fortune may go you or I.

3. Show me the whiskey that stains on the floor,
   Show me a drunken man as he stumbles out the door,
   And I'll show you a young man with many reasons why,
   And there but for fortune may go you or I.

4. Show me a country where the bombs had to fall,
   Show me the ruins of the buildings once so tall,
   And I'll show you a young land with so many reasons why,
   And there but for fortune may go you or I, or I.

New York State Of Mind

Words and Music: Billy Joel

Slowly

Some folks like to get a-way, take a hol-i-day from the neigh-bor-hood,
Seen all those mov-ie stars and their fan-cy cars and their lim-ou-sines,

hop a flight to Mi-a-mi Beach or to Hol-ly-wood.
been high in the Rock-ies un-der the ev-er-greens.

But I'm tak-in' a Grey-hound on the Hud-son Riv-er line,—
But I know what I'm need-in' and I don't wan-na waste more time,—

I'm in a New York state of mind.

mind.

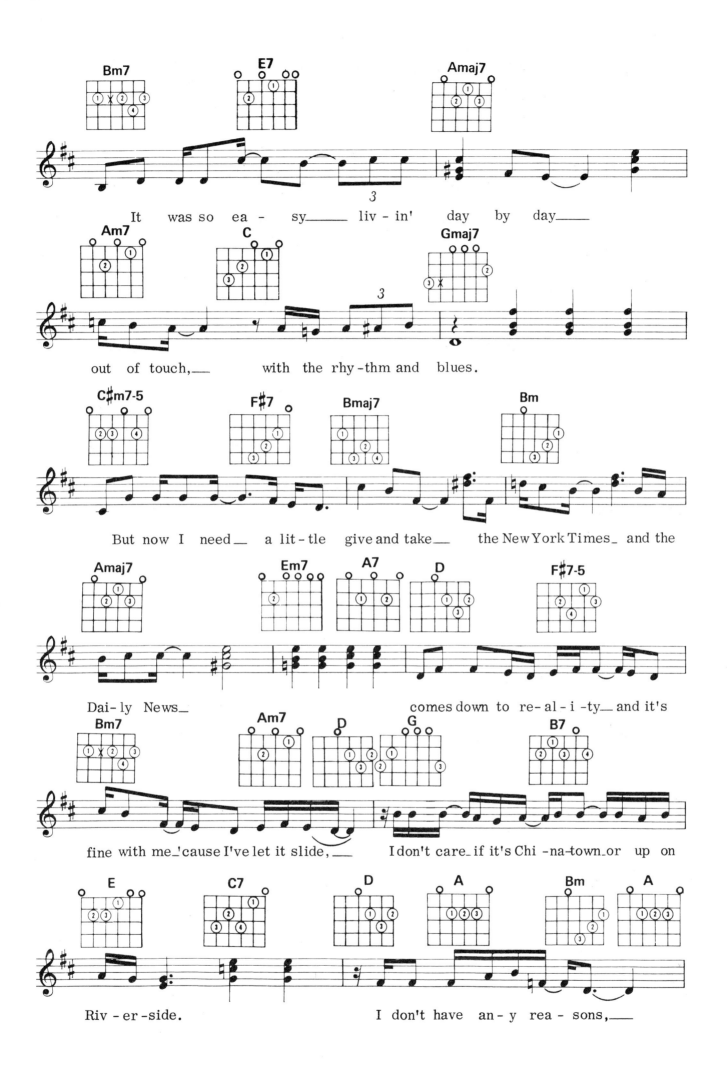

Movin' Out

Words and Music: Billy Joel

An - tho - ny works__ in the gro - cer - y store__
Ser - geant O'- Leary__ is walk-in' the beat__ At

sav - in' his pen - nies for some - day.
night he be - comes__ a bar - ten - der. He works at

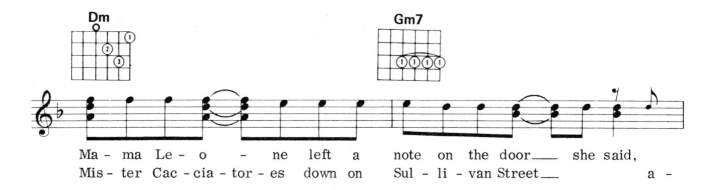

Ma – ma Le – o – ne left a note on the door — she said,
Mis – ter Cac – cia – tor – es down on Sul – li – van Street — a –

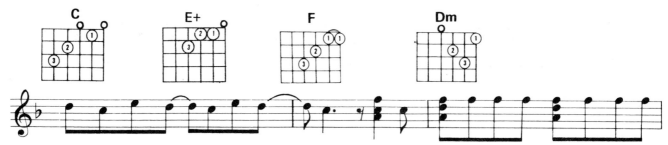

"Son – ny move out — to the coun – try." Ah but work-ing too hard can give you a
cross from the med – i – cal cen – ter. And he's trad -in' in his Chev-y for a

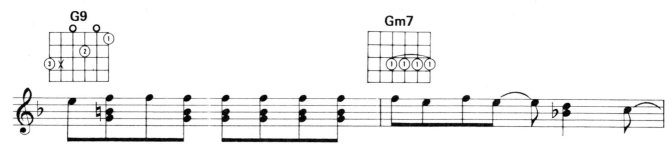

heart at – tack ack, ack, ack, ack, ack, You ought to know — by now. —
Cad – il – lac ack, ack, ack, ack, ack, You ought to know — by now. —

— Who needs a house — out in Hack-en sack? Is
— if he can't drive — with a bro -ken back At

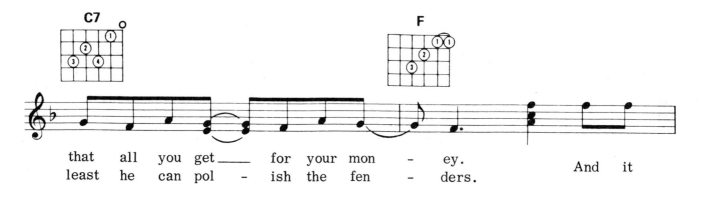

that all you get —— for your mon – ey. And it
least he can pol – ish the fen – ders.

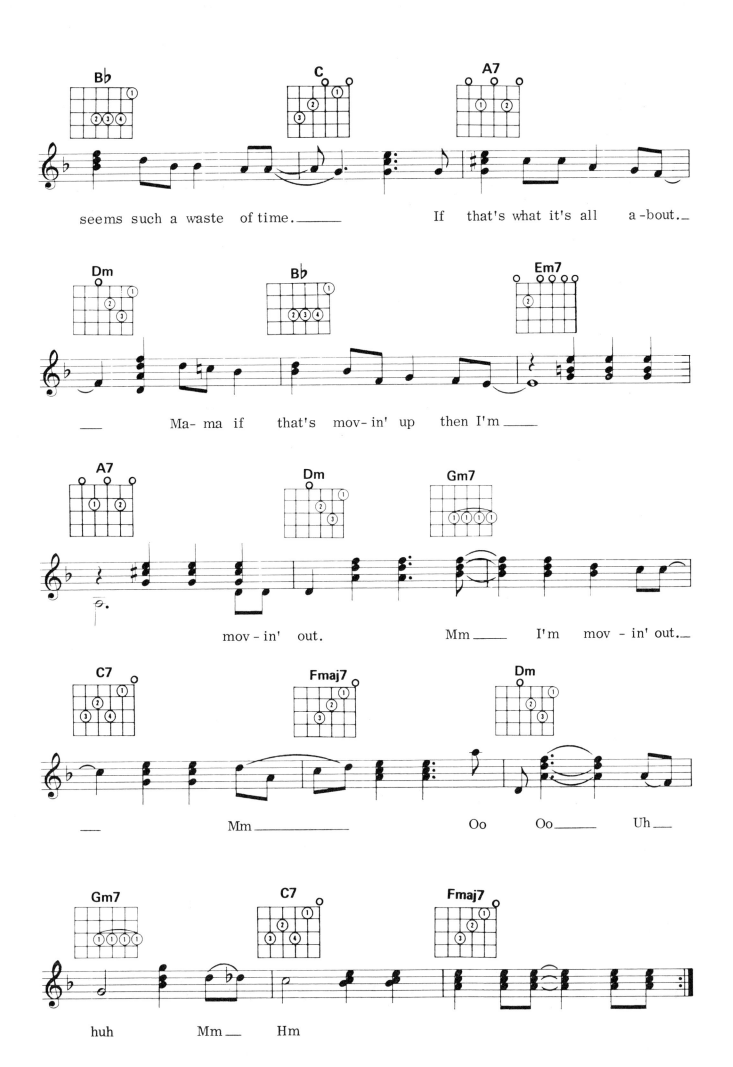

seems such a waste of time._____ If that's what it's all a -bout.___

__ Ma- ma if that's mov- in' up then I'm _____

mov - in' out. Mm_____ I'm mov - in' out.___

__ Mm_____ Oo Oo_____ Uh __

huh Mm __ Hm

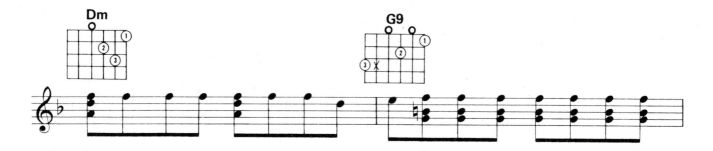

you should nev er ar - gue with a cra - zy mi, mi, mi, mi, mi, mind,

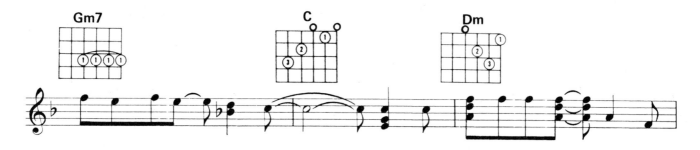

You ought to know__ by now._____ You can pay Un - cle Sam__ with the

ov - er time Is that all you get__ for your mon - ey. And if

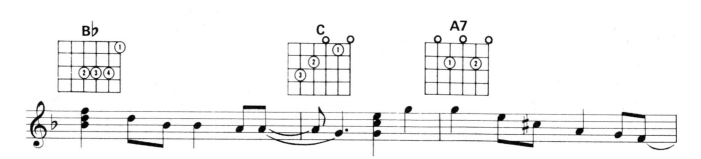

that's what you have in mind._____ Then that's what you're all a - bout.__

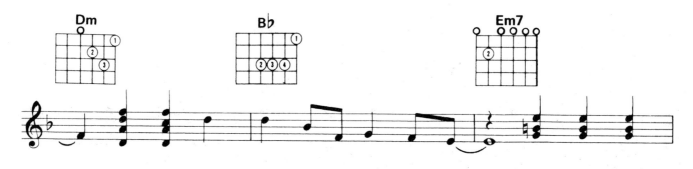

__ Good luck mov - in' up 'cause I'm ____

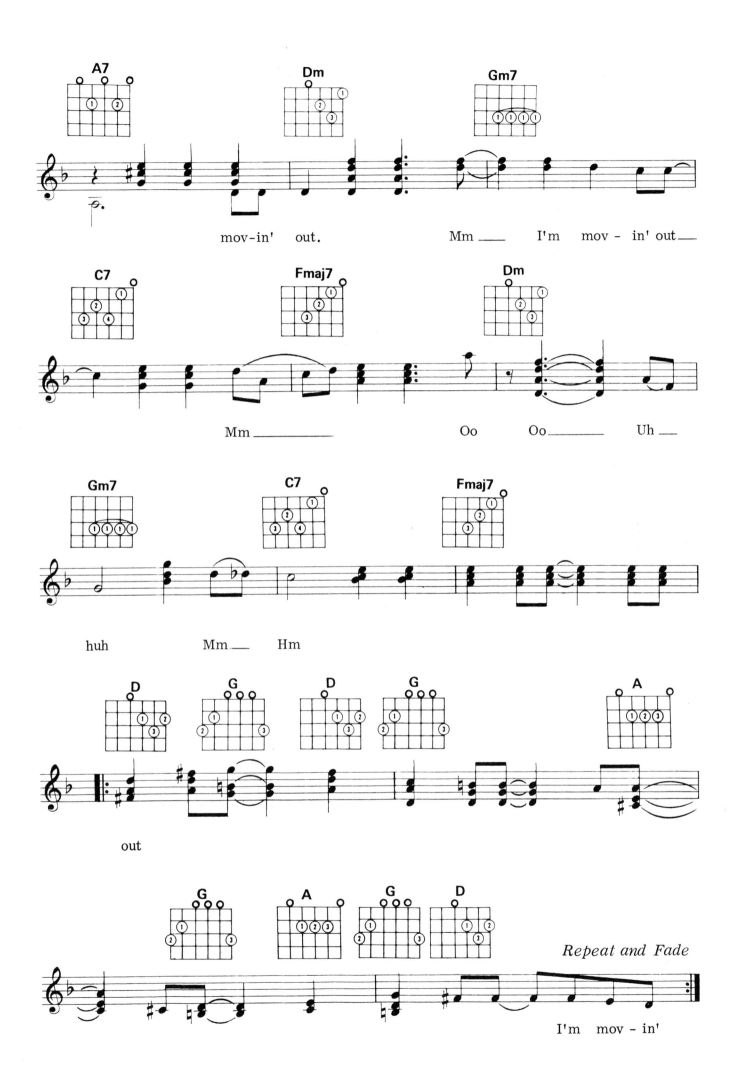

mov-in' out.   Mm ___   I'm   mov - in' out ___

Mm _____   Oo   Oo _____   Uh ___

huh   Mm ___ Hm

out

Repeat and Fade

I'm   mov - in'

The Entertainer

Words and Music: Billy Joel

Moderate

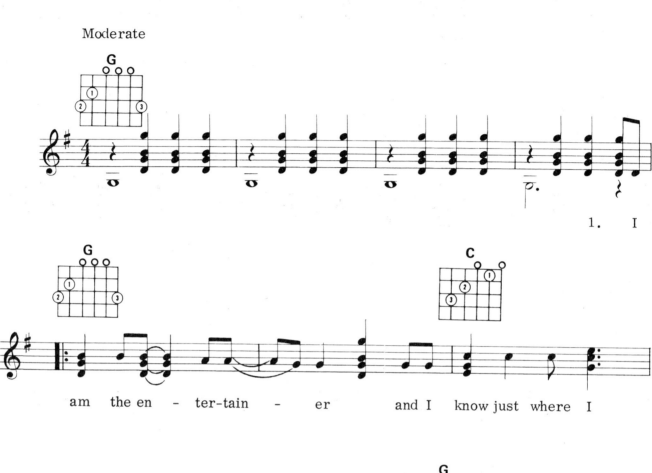

1. I

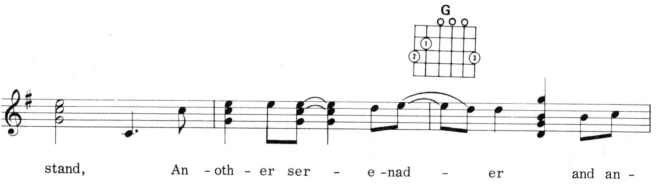

am the en - ter-tain - er and I know just where I

stand, An -oth - er ser - e -nad - er and an -

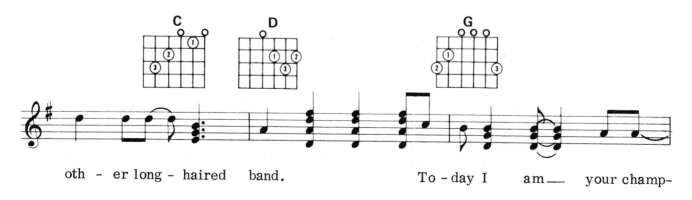

oth - er long - haired band. To -day I am your champ-

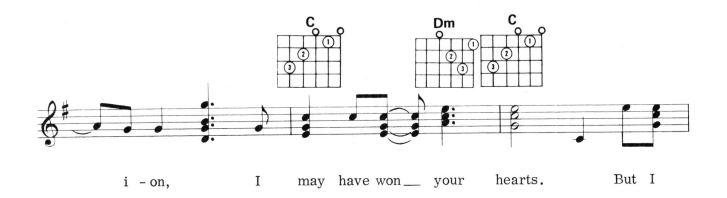

i - on,   I   may   have   won ___ your   hearts.   But I

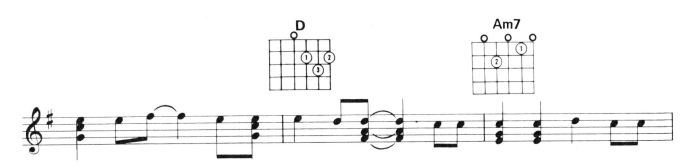

know   the   game ___ you'll   for - get   my   name, ___ And I   won't   be   here   in   an -

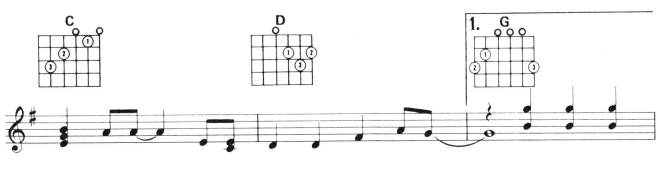

oth - er   year ___ If   I   don't   stay   on   the   charts. ___

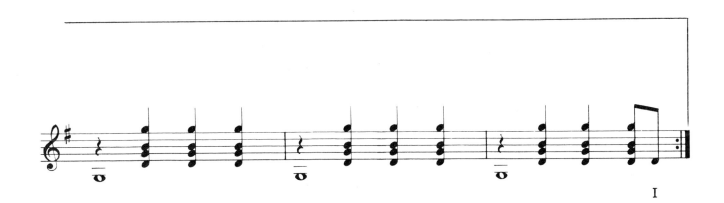

I

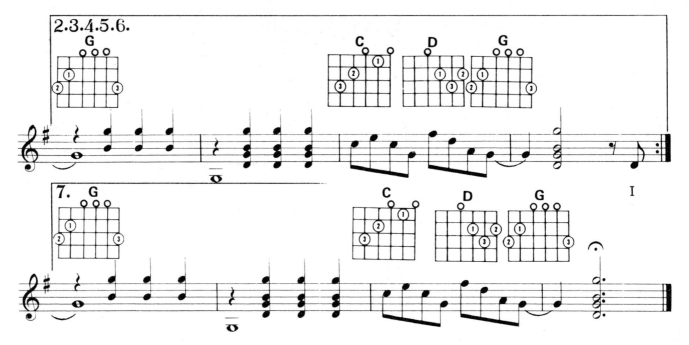

2. I am the entertainer and I've had to pay my price,
   The things I did not know at first I learned by doing twice.
   But still they come to haunt me, still they want their say,
   So I've learned to dance with a hand in my pants
   And I rub my neck and write 'em a check
   And they go their merry way.

3. I am the entertainer, been all around the world,
   I've played all kinds of palaces and laid all kinds of girls.
   I can't remember faces, I don't remember names,
   But what the hell, you know it's just as well
   'cause after awhile and a thousand miles
   It all becomes the same.

4. I am the entertainer, I bring to you my songs,
   I'd like to spend a day or two but I can't stay that long.
   I got to meet expenses, I got to stay in line,
   Got to get those fees to the agencies
   And I'd love to stay but there's bills to pay
   So I just don't have the time.

5. I am the entertainer, I've come to do my show,
   You've heard my latest record spin on the radio.
   It took me years to write it, they were the best years of my life,
   If you're gonna have a hit you gotta make it fit
   So they cut it down to 3:05.

6. I am the entertainer, the idol of my age,
   I make all kinds of money when I go on the stage.
   You see me in the papers, I've been in the magazines,
   But if I go cold, I won't get sold,
   I get put in the back in the discount rack
   Like another can of beans.

7. I am the entertainer and I know just where I stand,
   Another serenader and another long-haired band.
   Today I am your champion, I may have won your hearts,
   But I know the game, You'll forget my name,
   I won't be here in another year
   If I don't stay on the charts.

Casey Jones

Words: Robert Hunter
Music: Jerry Garcia

Switch-man's sleep - ing, Train Hun - dred and Two ___ is
on the wrong track and head - ed for you. ___
Driv - ing that train, ___ high on co - caine, ___
Ca - sey Jones, you'd bet - ter watch your speed. ___
Trou - ble a - head, ___ trou - ble be - hind, ___
and you know that no - tion just crossed my mind. just crossed my mind. ___
And you know that no - tion just crossed my mind. ___

Truckin'

Words: Robert Hunter
Music: Jerry Garcia, Bob Weir & Phil Lesh

Truck-in' like the doo-dah-man once told me, "You got to play your hand. Some-times the cards ain't worth a dime if you don't lay 'em down."

Some-times the lights all shine-in' on me, oth-er times I can bare-ly see.

Late-ly it oc-curs to me, what a long strange trip it's been.

To Coda

103

What in the world ev-er be came of sweet Jane?
Sit-tin' and starin' out of the ho-tel win-dow,
She

lost her spar-kle you know she is-n't the same.
got a tip they're gon-na kick the door in a-gain.
I'd

Liv-in' on reds, vit-a-min C,__ and co-caine,
like to get some sleep be fore I trav-el,
but if

all a friend can say is ain't it a shame.__
you got a war-rant I guess you're gon-na come in.__

Truck-in' up to Buf-fa-lo, been think-in' you got to mel-low slow.__
Bust-ed down on Bour-bon Street. Set up like a bowl-in' pin.__

Takes time, you pick a place__ to go, just keep truck-in' on.__
Knocked down, it gets to wear-in'__ thin, they just won't let you be.__

104

Dark Star

Words: Robert Hunter
Music: Jerry Garcia, Mickey Hart, Bill Kreutzmann, Phil Lesh,
Ron McKernan & Bob Weir

Playing In The Band

Words: Robert Hunter
Music: Bob Weir & Mickey Hart

Additional lyrics

2. Some folks look for answers,
   Others look for fights,
   Some folks up in tree tops,
   Just to look to see the sights.
   I can tell your future.
   Whoa, just look what's in your hand.
   But, I can't stop for nothing.
   I'm just playing in the band.

   Chorus

3. Standing on a tower,
   World at my command.
   You just keep a-turning,
   While I'm playing in the band.
   If a man among you
   Got no sin upon his hand,
   Let him cast a stone at me,
   For playing in the band.

   Chorus

My Sweet Lord

Words and Music: George Harrison

The Fifty-Ninth Street Bridge Song (Feelin' Groovy)

Words and Music by Paul Simon

Slow down,_ you move too fast;_ you got to make the
Hel - lo___ lamppost, what - cha know-in'?_ I've come to watch your

morn-ing last. Just kick - in' down the cob - ble stones,_
flow - ers grow- in'. Ain't-cha got no rhymes for me?___

look-in' for fun and feel-in' groov-y._
Doot - in' doo doo, feel-in' groov-y._

Got no deeds to do, no prom - is - es to keep. I'm

dap-pled and drow-sy and read-y to sleep. Let the morn -ing-time drop all its pet-als on me.

Life, I love you. All is groov-y._

Me And Julio Down By The Schoolyard

Words and Music: Paul Simon

saw,   it was a-gainst the law.___   The

ma - ma looked down and spit on the ground ev - 'ry
cou - ple of days they come and take me a - way but the

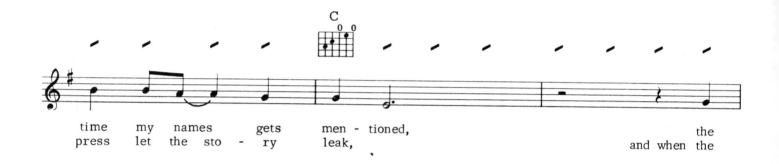

time my names gets men - tioned,   the
press let the sto - ry leak,   and when the

pa - pa said, "Oy, if I get that boy___ I'm gon - na stick him in the house of de - ten -
rad - i - cal priest come to get me re - leased we's all on the cov - er of News-

tion." }
week. }
     Well, I'm on my way,

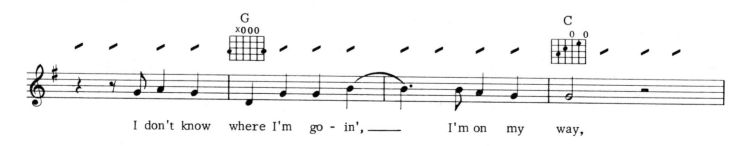

I don't know where I'm go - in', ___ I'm on my way,

Slip Slidin' Away

Words and Music: Paul Simon

you is so o-ver-pow-'ring I'm a-fraid ___ that I will dis-ap-pear."

1. Slip slid-in' a-

2. Slip slid-in' a-way,

slip slid-in' a-way. _____

You know the near-er your des-ti-na-tion the more ___ you're slip slid-in' a-way. _____

2. And I know a fa-ther ___ who had a son. He longed to tell him all the rea-sons for the things he'd done. He came a long way _____ just to ex-plain. _____ He kissed his

Additional lyrics

2. I know a woman became a wife.
   These are the very words she uses to describe her life.
   She said, "A good day ain't got no rain."
   She said, "A bad day is when I lie in bed and think
         of things that might have been."

   (Chorus)

3. God only knows, God makes His plan.
   The information is unavailable to the mortal man.
   We work our jobs, collect our pay.
   Believe we are gliding down the highway when in fact
         we are slip slidin' away.

   (Chorus)

Still Crazy After All These Years

Words and Music: Paul Simon

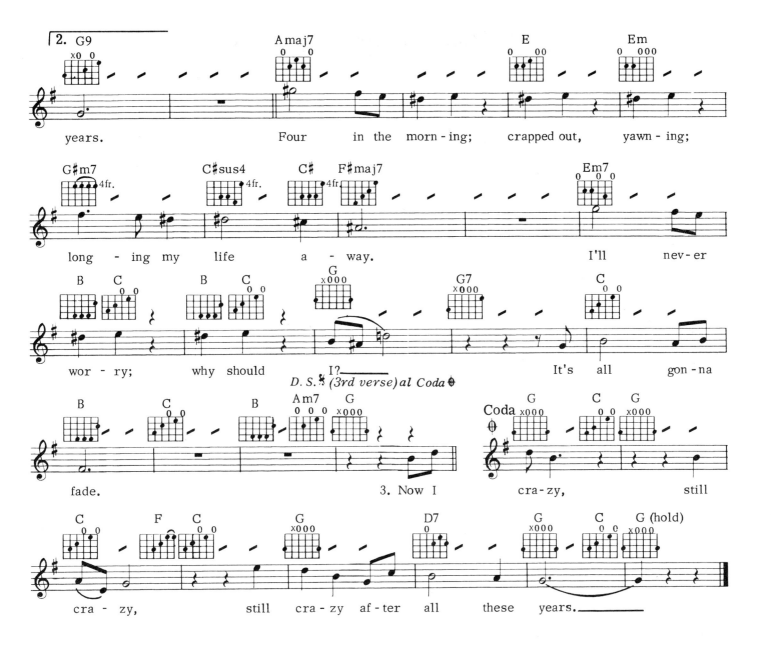

Additional lyrics

2. I'm not the kind of man who tends to socialize;
   I seem to lean on old familiar ways.
   And I ain't no fool for love songs that whisper in my ears,
   Still crazy after all these years;
   Oh, still crazy after all these years.

3. Now I sit by my window and I watch the cars;
   I fear I'll do some damage one fine day.
   But I would not be convicted by a jury of my peers.
   Still crazy after all these years;
   Oh, still crazy, still crazy,
   Still crazy after all these years.

Fifty Ways To Leave Your Lover

Words and Music by Paul Simon

Moderately

1. "The prob-lem's all in - side your head," she said to me;
2. She said, "It grieves me now to see you in such pain; I wish

"The an - swer is eas - y if you take it log - i - c'lly.
there was some - thin' I could do to make you smile a - gain."

I'm here to help you if you're strug - glin' to be free; there must be
I said, "I ap - pre-ci-ate that, and could you please ex - plain a - bout the

fif - ty ways to leave your lov - er."
fif-ty ways?"

She said,"It's real-ly not my
She said,"Why don't we both just

hab - it to in - trude; I hope my mean - ing won't be
sleep on it to - night; I'm sure in the morn - ing you'll be -

lost or mis - con - strued. But I'll re - peat my - self at the
gin to see the light." And then she kissed me and I re - a - lized she

Mother And Child Reunion

Words and Music: Paul Simon

Moderately

Chorus

No, I would not give you false hope, on this strange and mourn - ful day, but the moth - er and child__ re - un - ion__ is on - ly a mo - tion a - way.

Verse

Oh, lit - tle dar - ling of mine,_

1. I can't for the
2. I just can't be -

life of me,___
lieve it's so,___

re - mem - ber a sad - der day,___
and though it seems strange to say,___

I know they say let it be,___
I nev - er been laid so low,___

but it just don't work
in such a mys - te -

out that way,   and the course of a   life - time runs
ri - ous way,   and the course of a   life - time runs

Chorus

o - ver and   o - ver a - gain.___   No, I
o - ver and   o - ver a - gain.___   But, I

would not   give you   false hope,   on this strange and mourn - ful

day,_____   when the moth - er and child_ re - un - ion is

on - ly a mo - tion a - way._____   Oh, the

moth - er and child_ re - un - ion   is   on - ly a mo - tion a

way.   Oh, the moth - er and child_ re - un - ion_ is

on - ly a mo - ment a - way._____

Mrs Robinson

Words and Music: Paul Simon

And here's to you, _____ ✱Mrs._ Rob - in - son, _

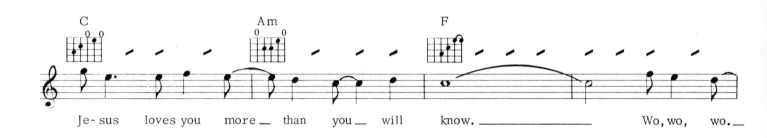

Je- sus loves you more _ than you _ will know. _____ Wo, wo, wo. _

_ God bless you please, _ Mrs._ Rob - in - son, _

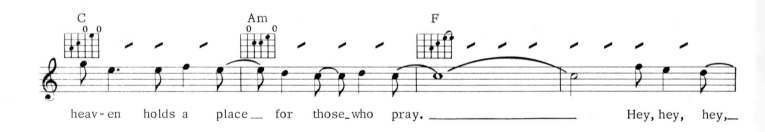

heav- en holds a place _ for those _ who pray. _____ Hey, hey, hey, _

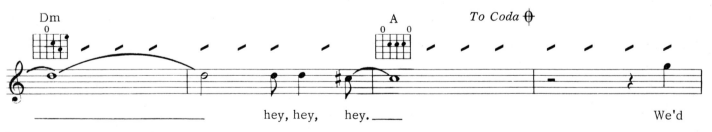

_____ hey, hey, hey. ____ We'd

✱ Mrs. is pronounced "Mis-sus".

like to know_ a lit – tle bit_ a - bout_ you for_ our files._____

___ We'd like to help_ you learn to help your - self. _____

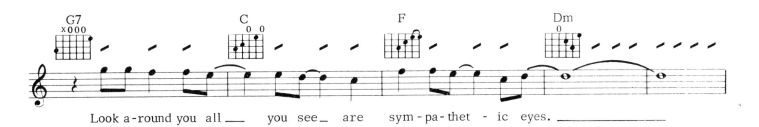

Look a-round you all ___ you see_ are sym-pa-thet - ic eyes. _____

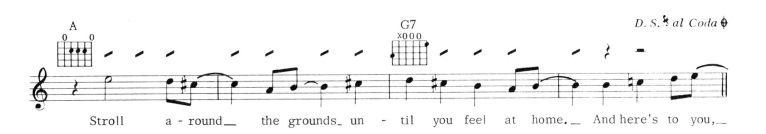

D. S. al Coda

Stroll a - round_ the grounds_ un – til you feel at home._ And here's to you,_

Coda

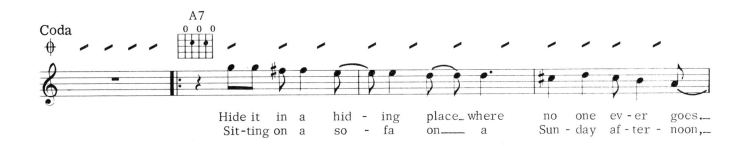

Hide it in a hid – ing place_ where no one ev-er goes._
Sit-ting on a so - fa on___ a Sun - day af-ter - noon,_

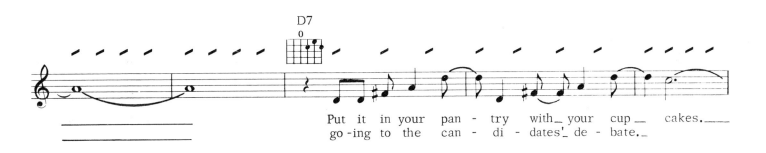

_____ Put it in your pan - try with_ your cup_ cakes._____
_____ go -ing to the can - di - dates'_ de - bate._

America

Words and Music: Paul Simon

walked off _____ to look for A - mer - - i -
moon rose _____ o - ver an o - pen

ca. _____
field. _____

"Kath - y," I said as we board - ed the Grey-hound in Pitts - burgh, _____
"Kath - y, I'm lost," I said though I knew she was sleep - ing, _____

"Mich - i - gan seems like a dream to me
"I'm emp - ty and ach - ing and I don't know

now. _____
why." _____

It took me four days to
Count - ing the cars on the

hitch-hike from Sag - i - naw, I've come _____ to look for A -
New Jer - sey Turn-pike, they've all come _____ to look for A -

To Coda

mer - i - ca." _____
mer - i - ca." _____

Cecilia

Words and Music: Paul Simon

My Little Town

Words and Music: Paul Simon

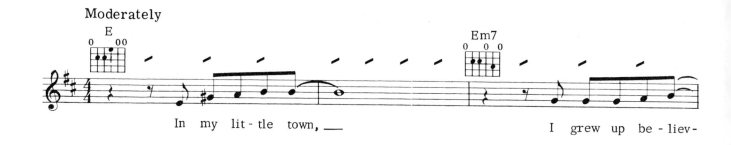

In my lit-tle town, ___ I grew up be - liev-

ing God keeps his eye ___ on us all.

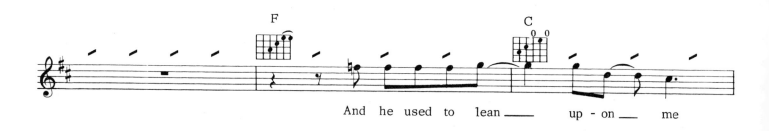

And he used to lean ___ up - on ___ me

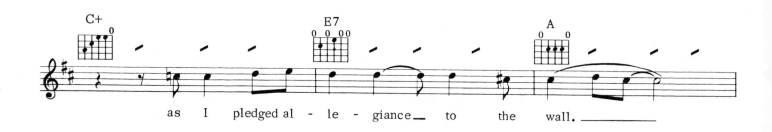

as I pledged al - le - giance ___ to the wall. ___

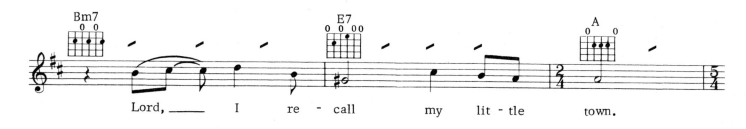

Lord, ___ I re - call my lit - tle town.

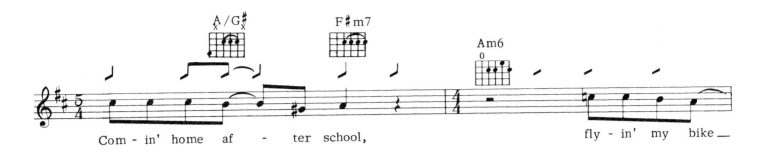

Com - in' home af - ter school, fly - in' my bike —

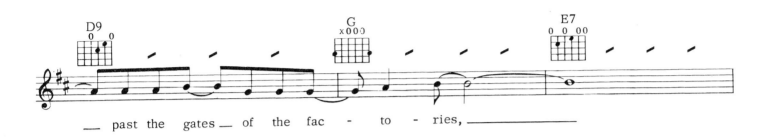

— past the gates — of the fac - to - ries, —

my mom do - ing the laun - dry, —

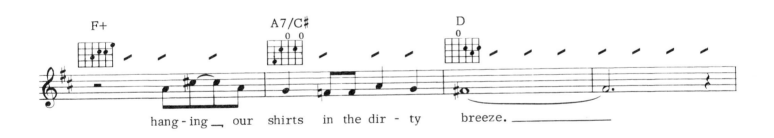

hang - ing — our shirts in the dir - ty breeze. —

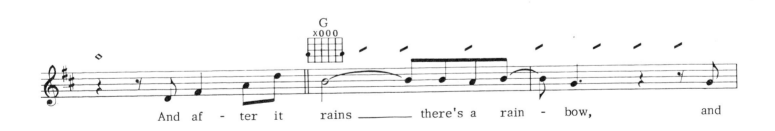

And af - ter it rains — there's a rain - bow, and

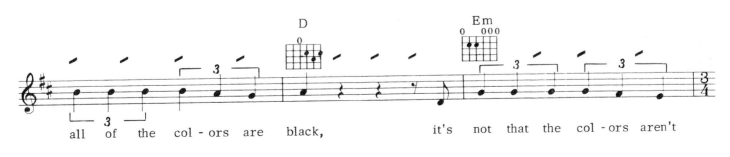

all of the col - ors are black, it's not that the col - ors aren't

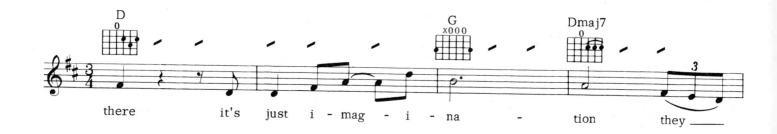

there   it's   just   i - mag - i - na - tion   they ____

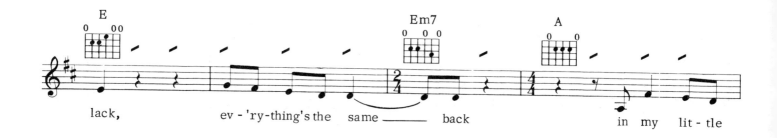

lack,   ev - 'ry-thing's the   same ____ back   in   my   lit - tle

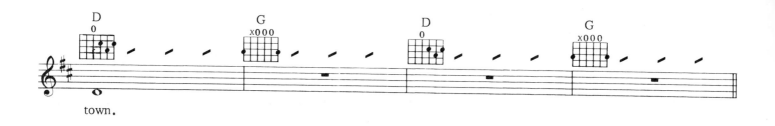

town.

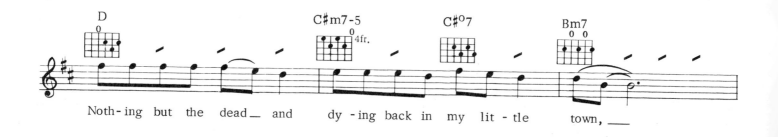

Noth - ing but the dead _ and   dy - ing back in my lit - tle   town, ____

noth - ing but the dead _ and   dy - ing back in   my _   lit - tle

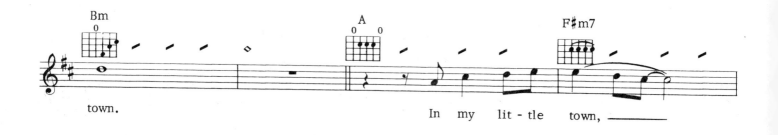

town.   In   my   lit - tle   town, _____

I nev-er meant noth - ing, I was just my __ fa - ther's son, __

mm. _____ Sav - ing my mon - ey, __

dream - ing of glo - ry, _____ twitch-ing like a

fin - ger __ on the trig - ger of __ a gun. _____

Leav-ing noth - ing but the dead __ and dy - ing back in my lit - tle

town, _____ noth - ing but the dead __ and

dy - ing back in my __ lit - tle town.

Feel Like A Number

Words and Music: Bob Seger

Bright Rock beat

I take my card ___ and I stand ___ in line. ___ To
work-ers, I'm ___ just an-oth-er drone. ___ To

make a buck, ___ I work o - ver-time. ___ "Dear Sir" let-ters keep com-
Ma Bell, I'm ___ just an-oth-er phone. ___ I'm just an-oth-er sta-tis-

ing in ___ the mail.
tic on ___ a sheet.
I
To

work my back ___ till it's wracked ___ with pain. ___ The boss can't e - ven re-call
teach-ers I'm ___ just an-oth - er child. ___ To I. R. S., ___ I'm an-oth-

___ my name. ___ I show up late ___ and I'm docked. ___ It nev - er fails.
er file. ___ I'm just an - oth - er con-sen - sus on ___ the street.

I feel just like an - oth - er
Gonna cruise out of this cit - y;

spike in a great big wheel; like a ti-ny blade of grass
head down to the sea. Gon-na shout out at the o-

in a great big field. To And I feel like a
cean, "Hey, it's me!"

num-ber. Feel like a num-ber. Feel like a

stran-ger, a stran-ger in this land. I feel like a

num-ber. I'm not a num-ber. I'm not a

num-ber. Damn it, I'm a man. I said I'm a man!

D. S. *and fade*

And I feel like a

139

Hollywood Nights

Words and Music: Bob Seger

Moderately bright Rock beat

1. She stood there, bright as the sun, on that Cal - i - for - nia coast.

He was a mid - west - ern boy on his own.

She looked at him with those soft eyes, so

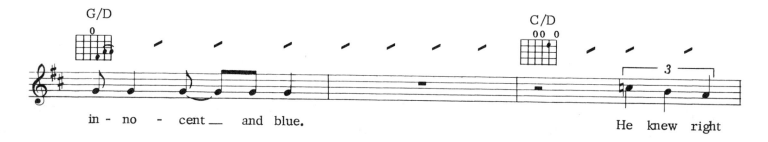

in - no - cent __ and blue. He knew right

then he was too far from home. And those Hol-

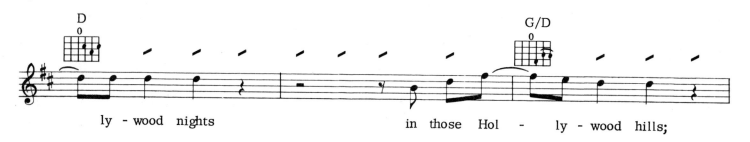

ly - wood nights in those Hol - ly - wood hills;

she was look-ing so right　in her dia — monds and frills.

Oh, those big ___ cit-y nights ___　in those high,___

___ roll-ing hills; ___　a-bove all the lights,

To Coda ⊕　D. C. (with repeats) al Coda ⊕　Coda

she had all ___ of her skills.

Additional lyrics

Verse 2.　She took his hand and she led him along that golden beach.
　　　　　They watched the waves tumble over the sand.
　　　　　They drove for miles and miles up those twisting, turning roads.
　　　　　Higher and higher and higher they climbed.

Chorus I.　And those Hollywood nights (etc.)

Verse 3.　He'd headed west 'cause he felt that a change would do him good.
　　　　　See some old friends, good for the soul.
　　　　　She had been born with a face that would let her get her way.
　　　　　He saw that face and he lost all control.

Verse 4.　Night after night and day after day it went on and on.
　　　　　Then came that morning he woke up alone.
　　　　　He spent all night staring down at the lights of L. A.,
　　　　　Wondering if he could ever go home.

Chorus II.　And those Hollywood nights in those Hollywood hills:
　　　　　It was looking so right. It was giving him chills.
　　　　　Oh, those big city nights in those high, rolling hills,
　　　　　Above all the lights with a passion that kills.

141

Against The Wind

Words and Music: Bob Seger

Additional lyrics

2. And the years rolled slowly past.
   And I found myself alone,
   Surrounded by strangers I thought were my friends.
   I found myself further and further from my home,
   And I guess I lost my way.
   There were oh so many roads.
   I was livin' to run and runnin' to live.
   Never worried about payin', or even how much I owed.
   Movin' eight miles a minute for months at a time,
   Breakin' all of the rules that would bend,
   I began to find myself searchin',
   Searchin' for shelter again and again.
   Against the wind,
   Little somethin' against the wind.
   I found myself seekin' shelter against the wind.

3. *Instrumental* _____
   _____
   _____
   _____
   _____
   _____
   _____
   _____

   Well, those drifter's days are past me now.
   I've got so much more to think about:
   Deadlines and commitments,
   What to leave in, what to leave out.
   Against the wind,
   I'm still runnin' against the wind.
   I'm older now, but still runnin' against the wind.
   Well, I'm older now, and still runnin' against the wind,
   Against the wind.

49 Bye-Byes

Words and Music: Stephen Stills

Moderately

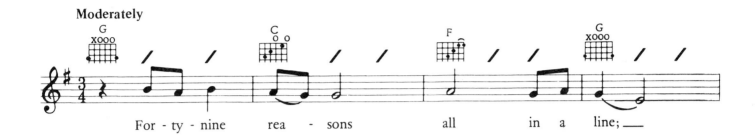

For - ty - nine rea - sons all in a line; ___

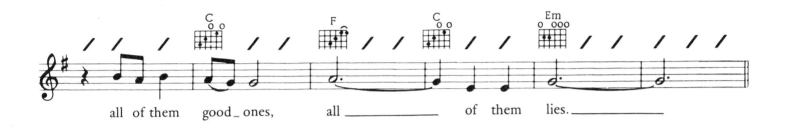

all of them good_ ones, all _____ of them lies. ___

Drift - ing with my la - dy, we're old - est of friends;_ need a lit - tle
Now it's o - ver, they left in the spring;_ her and the

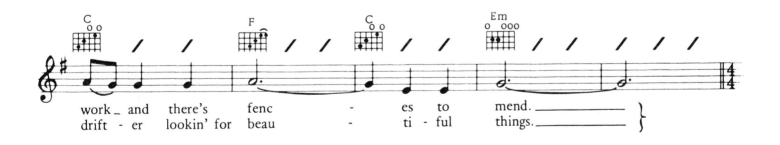

work_ and there's fenc - es to mend. _____
drift - er lookin' for beau - ti - ful things. _____

Stead-y girl, be my world;_ till the drift-er come,_ now she's gone. _

I let that man play his hand;__ I let them go, how was I to

know?__ I'm down__ on__ my__ knees.__ No - bod - y left__ to

please.__ No - bod - y left__ to

please.__ On my knees__ feel - ing wrong,__

my mind's gone,__ oh._____

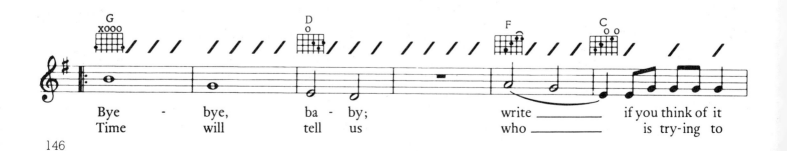

Bye - bye, ba - by; write_____ if you think of it
Time will tell us who_____ is try-ing to

For What It's Worth

Words and Music: Stephen Stills

3.

A/E ∅∅ ∅

E ∅ ∅∅

A/E ∅∅

4. Par - a -noi - a strikes   deep,

E ∅ ∅∅

A/E ∅∅

in - to   your life   it will   creep.   It

E ∅ ∅∅

A/E ∅∅

starts   when you're al - ways a - fraid,___   step out   of

E ∅ ∅∅

A/E ∅∅ ∅

line   the men come ___   and   take you a - way.___   You bet-ter

Repeat and fade

E ∅ ∅∅

D ∅

A ∅ ∅∅

G ∅∅∅

stop,   hey,___ what's that sound?_ Ev-'ry-bod-y look what's go - in' down. You bet-ter

2. There's battle lines bein' drawn, nobody's right if everybody's wrong.
   Young people speakin' their minds, gettin' so much resistance from behind.
                    (Chorus)

3. ·What a field day for the heat, a thousand people in the street
   Singin' songs and carryin' signs, mostly saying "Hooray for our side."
                    (Chorus)

Suite: Judy Blue Eyes

Words and Music: Stephen Stills

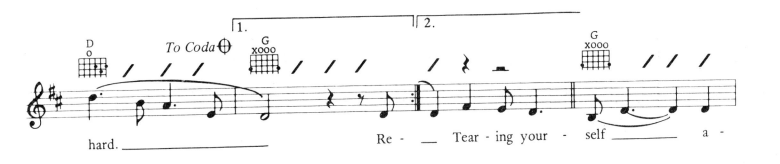

hard. _____ Re - __ Tear - ing your - self _____ a -

way from me now, you are free ____ and I am

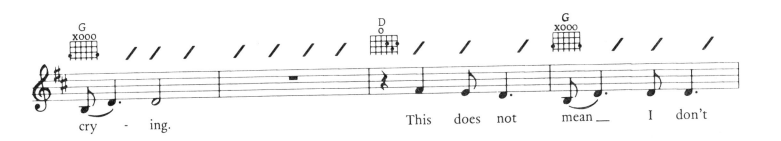

cry - ing. This does not mean __ I don't

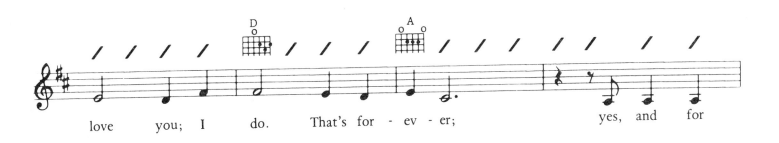

love you; I do. That's for - ev - er; yes, and for

al - ways.__ I am yours, you are mine, you are

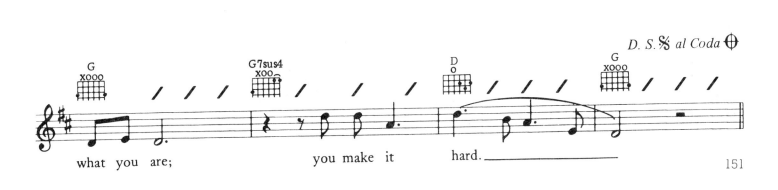

what you are; you make it hard._____

Coda

_ And you make it hard. _____

Fri - day
Tues - day

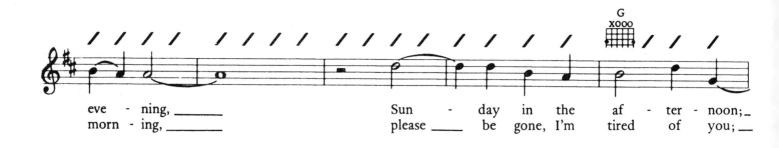

eve - ning, _____

morn - ing, _____

Sun - day in the af - ter - noon; _

please ____ be gone, I'm tired of you; _

_

_

what have you got to lose? _____

what have you got to lose? _____

1.   2.

Can I tell it like it is? _____

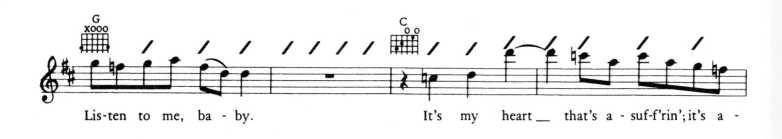

Lis-ten to me, ba - by.

It's my heart __ that's a - suf-f'rin'; it's a -

dy - in' and that's what I ___ have to lose.

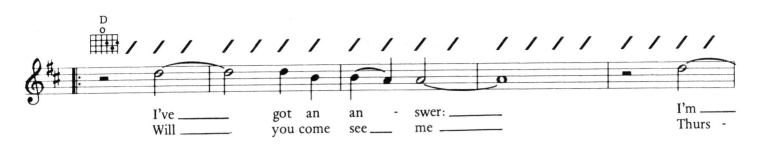

I've _____ got an an - swer: _____ I'm _____ Thurs -
Will _____ you come see ___ me _____

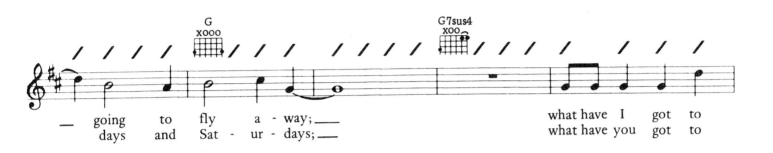

_ going to fly a - way; ___ what have I got to
days and Sat - ur - days; ___ what have you got to

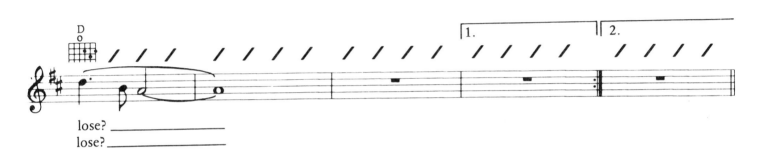

1.

lose? _____
lose? _____

2.

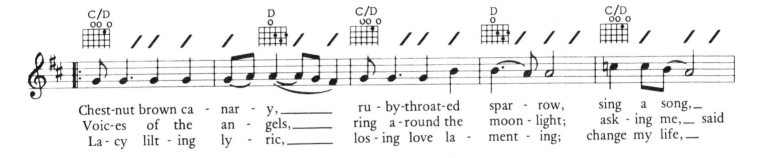

Chest-nut brown ca - nar - y, _____ ru - by-throat-ed spar - row, sing a song, _
Voic-es of the an - gels, _____ ring a - round the moon - light; ask - ing me, _ said
La - cy lilt - ing ly - ric, _____ los - ing love la - ment - ing; change my life, _

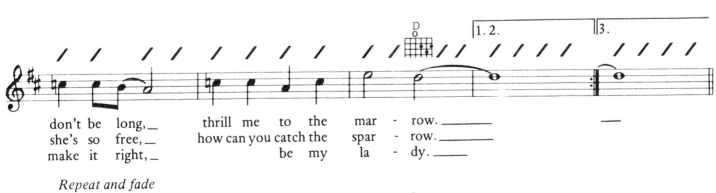

1. 2.

3.

don't be long, _ thrill me to the mar - row. _____
she's so free, _ how can you catch the spar - row. _____
make it right, _ be my la - dy. _____

Repeat and fade

Du du du du du du du du du du du, du du du du du du du du du.

China Grove

Words and Music: Tom Johnston

ev - 'ry day__ there's a new thing__ com - in', the ways of the O - ri - en - tal

view.__ The sher - iff and his bud - dies with their sam - u - rai swords,__

you can e - ven hear the mu - sic at __ night.____

And though it's a part of the Lone Star State,__

peo - ple don't seem __ to care: they just keep on

look - in' to the East.__

Talk - in' 'bout the Chi - na Grove,__ oh, _____

Chi - na Grove.

Takin' It To The Streets
Words and Music: Michael McDonald

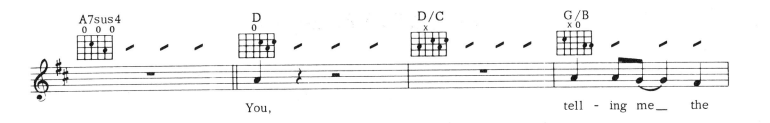

You, tell - ing me_ the

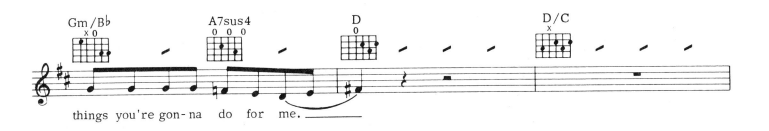

things you're gon- na do for me. _____

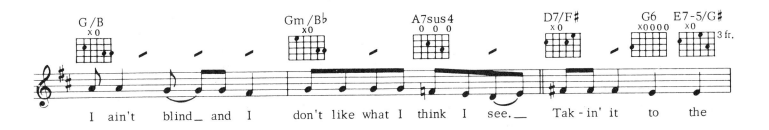

I ain't blind_ and I don't like what I think I see._ Tak - in' it to the

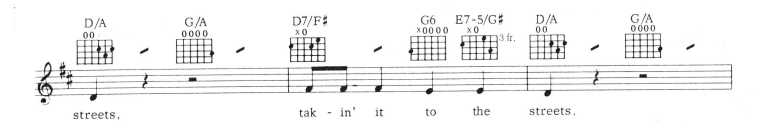

streets, tak - in' it to the streets,

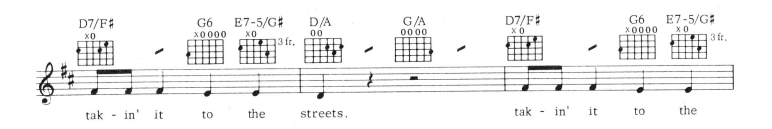

tak - in' it to the streets, tak - in' it to the

Repeat and fade

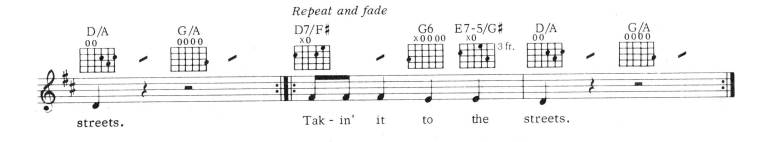

streets. Tak - in' it to the streets.

What A Fool Believes

Words and Music: Michael McDonald & Kenny Loggins

Cat's In The Cradle

Words and Music: Harry Chapin & Sandy Chapin

Moderate Folk style

Verse

1. My child ar-rived __ just the oth-er day; he

came to the world in the u-su-al way.__ But there were

planes to catch __ and bills to pay;__ he learned to walk while I

was a-way. And he was talk-in' 'fore I knew it, and

as he grew he'd say, "I'm gon-na be like you, Dad, you

Chorus

know I'm gon-na be like you."

And the

cat's in the cra-dle and the sil - ver spoon, ___ lit - tle boy blue and the man in the moon. ___ "When you com -in' home {Dad?" Dad?" Son?" Son?"} "I don't know when, but we'll get to-geth-er then; ___ you know we'll have a good time then."

1.2.3. then."

4. Verse (hold) 2. My then."

2. My son turned ten just the other day; he said, "Thanks for the ball, Dad; come on, let's play.
Can you teach me to throw?" I said, "Not today, I got a lot to do." He said, "That's okay."
And he walked away, but his smile never dimmed, it said:
I'm gonna be like him, yeah, you know I'm gonna be like him.
(Chorus)

3. Well, he came from college just the other day; so much like a man I just had to say,
"Son, I'm proud of you, can you sit for a while?" He shook his head and he said with a smile,
"What I'd really like, Dad, is to borrow the car keys;
See you later, can I have them please?"
(Chorus)

4. I've long since retired, my son's moved away; I called him up just the other day.
I said, "I'd like to see you if you don't mind." He said, "I'd love to, Dad, if I can find the time.
You see, my new job's a hassle and the kids have the flu,
But it's sure nice talkin' to you, Dad, it's been sure nice talkin' to you.
And as I hung up the phone it occurred to me,
He'd grown up just like me; my boy was just like me.
(Chorus)

W.O.L.D.

Words and Music: Harry Chapin

A M rock_ but I just had to run a-round.__ It's been eight years_ since I left you, babe; let me tell you, 'bout what's gone down. I am the morn-ing D J at W O L D, D, D, D, (dou-ble u) D, D, D, D, play-ing all the hits for you wher-ev-er you may be. The bright "Good Morn-ing" voice who's heard but nev-er seen, feel-ing·all of for-ty-five___

1.
go-ing on fif-teen.__

2. The

2.

teen._

I'm mak-ing ex-tra mon-ey do-ing high school sock hops; I'm the big time guest em-cee._ You should hear me talk-ing to the lit-tle chil-dren and lis-ten what they say to me. I got a spot on the top of my head just beg-ging for a new tou-pee. There's a tire a-round my gut from sit-ting on my, but it's nev-er gon-na go a-way._

D.S. % al Coda ⊕

Additional lyrics

2. The drinking I did on my last big gig, it made my voice go low.
They said that they liked the young sound when they let me go.
So I drifted on down to Tulsa, Oklahoma to do me a late night talk show.
Now I've worked my way down home again to Boise, Idaho.

3. Sometimes I get this crazy dream that I just take off in my car.
But you can travel ten thousand miles and still stay where you are.
Thinking that I should stop this jockeying and start that record store;
Maybe I could settle down if you take me back once more.

Blondes Have More Fun

Words and Music: Rod Stewart and Jim Cregan

Fast shuffle beat

Is it a mat-ter of o-pin-ion
rose in Tex - as.
or just a
She gim-me

con - tra-dic - tion?
plen - ty of prac-tice.
But from where I come from,
But I couldn't touch the sur-face
all the
'cause of a

blondes have more fun.
re - cent face lift.
Well, just watch them sis - ters on a
She had no i - dea what

Sat - ur-day night;__ per - ox - ide__ caus-in' all of the fights.__ Oh
love's all a - bout 'ccpt a one o' - clock call on the cast - ing couch.__ Oh

yeah,
yeah,
oh,__ yeah.
oh,__ yeah.

1.
I took a

2.

Sis - sy from New York
crush__ on Bar - dot.
was on the
Fell in

The Killing Of Georgie (Part I and II)

Words and Music: Rod Stewart

Moderately slow, in 2

1. In these days_ of chang-ing ways,_ so called lib-er-at-ed days,_ a sto-ry comes_ to mind_ of a friend of mine.

Georg-ie boy_ was gay, I guess._ Noth-in' more or noth-in' less._ The kind-est guy I ev-er knew._

[1.-8.] 2. His

Slowly, in 2

[9.] Oh, Georg-ie,

Repeat and fade

stay;_ don't go_ a-way._

Georg-ie,_ please stay;_ you take my_ breath a-way._

Oh, Georg-ie,

Additional lyrics

2. His mother's tears fell in vain
   The afternoon George tried to explain
   That he needed love like all the rest.
   Pa said, "There must be a mistake.
   How can my son not be straight
   After all I've said and done for him?"

3. Leavin' home on a Greyhound bus,
   Cast out by the ones he loves,
   A victim of these gay days, it seems.
   Georgie went to New York town,
   Where he quickly settled down
   And soon became the toast of the Great White Way.

4. Accepted by Manhattan's elite
   In all the places that were chic,
   No party was complete without George.
   Along the boulevards he'd cruise
   And all the old queens blew a fuse;
   Everybody loved Georgie boy.

5. The last time I saw George alive
   Was in the summer of '75.
   He said he was in love; I said, "I'm pleased."
   George attended the opening night
   Of another Broadway hype,
   But split before the final curtain fell.

6. Deciding to take a shortcut home,
   Arm in arm, they meant no wrong;
   A gentle breeze blew down Fifth Avenue.
   Out of a darkened side street came
   A New Jersey gang with just one aim:
   To roll some innocent passerby.

7. There ensued a fearful fight;
   Screams rung out in the night.
   Georgie's head hit a sidewalk cornerstone.
   A leather kid, a switchblade knife,
   He did not intend to take his life;
   He just pushed his luck a little too far that night.

8. The sight of blood dispersed the gang;
   A crowd gathered, the police came,
   An ambulance screamed to a halt on Fifty-third and Third.
   Georgie's life ended there,
   But I ask, who really cares?
   George once said to me, and I quote:

9. He said: "Never wait or hesitate.
   Get in, kid, before it's too late;
   You may never get another chance,
   Cause youth's a mask, but it don't last.
   Live it long and live it fast."
   Georgie was a friend of mine.

You're In My Heart

Words and Music: Rod Stewart

trac-tion was — pure-ly phys-i-cal. you. You're in my
heart cried out — for —

heart; you're in — my soul. You'd be my breath should I — grow old. You are my

lov-er: you're my— best friend. You're in my soul. —

My love for you — is im-meas-ur-a-ble; — my re-
es-say in glam-our. Please par-don the gram-mar, but you're

spect for you— im- mense. You're age-less, time-less,
ev-'ry school-boy's dream. You're Cel-tic united,

lace and fine-ness; you're beau-ty and — el-e-
but, ba-by, I've de-cided you're the best team I've ever

gance.
seen.

You're a rhap - so - dy, ___ a com - e - dy; ___ you're a
And there have been ___ man - y af - fairs and

sym - pho - ny ___ and a play.
man - y times ___ I've thought to leave.

You're ev - 'ry love ___ song
But I bite my lip and

ev - er writ - ten, ___ but, hon - ey, what do you see in me?
turn a - round, ___ 'cause you're the warm - est thing I've ever found.

You're in my

heart; you're in ___ my soul. You'd be my breath should I ___ grow

old. You are my lov - er; you're my ___ best friend. You're in my

soul. ___

1. You're an

2.

Rocket Man

Words and Music: Elton John & Bernie Taupin

Moderately

so much I miss my wife,_____

it's lone - ly out__ in space _____

on such a time -

less__ flight._____

Chorus And I think it's gon - na be a long,__long time__ till touch - down brings_

And I think it's gon-na be a long, long time.

2. Mars ain't the kind of place to raise your kids,
   In fact it's cold as hell,
   And there's no one there to raise them if you did.
   And all this science I don't understand,
   It's just my job five days a week,
   A rocket man, a rocket man.
                    (Chorus)

Longer Boats

Words and Music: Cat Stevens

Peace Train

Words and Music: Cat Stevens

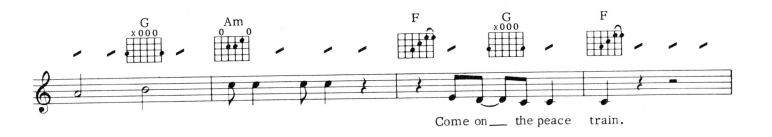

Come on__ the peace train.

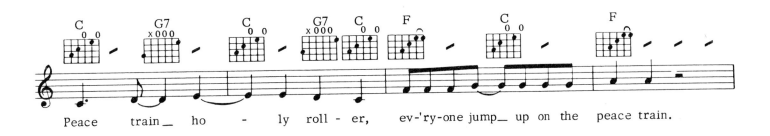

Peace train__ ho - ly roll - er, ev-'ry-one jump__ up on the peace train.

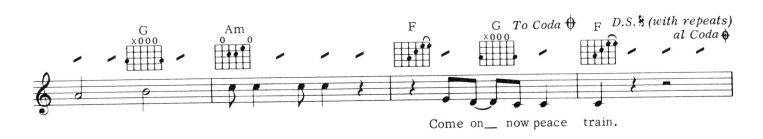

To Coda ⊕ *D.S.* 𝄋 *(with repeats) al Coda* ⊕

Come on__ now peace train.

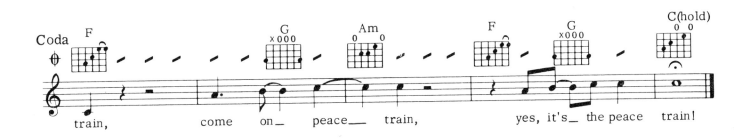

Coda ⊕

train, come on__ peace__ train, yes, it's__ the peace train!

Additional lyrics

2. Oh I've been smilin' lately
   Dreamin' about the world as one
   And I believe it could be
   Someday it's gonna come

4. Now I've been smilin' lately
   Thinkin' about the good things to come
   And I believe it could be
   Something good has begun

5. Get your bags together
   Go bring your good friends too
   Because it's getting nearer
   It soon will be with you

6. Oh come and join the living
   It's not so far from you
   And it's getting nearer
   Soon it will all be true

7. (Instrumental)_____
   _____
   _____
   _____

8. Now I've been cryin' lately
   Thinkin' about the world as it is
   Why must we go on hating
   Why can't we live in bliss.

For You Blue

Words and Music: George Harrison

Be - cause you're sweet _ and love - ly, girl, I
want you in _____ the morn - ing, girl, I

love you.
love you.

Be - cause you're sweet _ and the
I want you at _____ the

love - ly girl,_ it's true.
mo - ment, I feel blue.- I'm

love you more _ than ev - er, girl,_ I do._____
liv - ing ev - 'ry mo - ment, girl,_ for you._____

I
I've

Here Comes The Sun

Words and Music: George Harrison

Piggies

Words and Music: George Harrison

Have you seen the lit - tle pig - gies crawl - ing in the dirt?
Have you seen the big - ger pig - gies in their starched white shirts?

And for all the lit - tle pig-gies life is get - ting worse.
You will find the big - ger pig-gies stir-ring up the dirt.

Al -ways hav-ing dirt to
Al -ways have clean shirts to

play a - round in.
play a - round in.

In their styes with all their back - ing

they don't care what goes on a - round.

In their eyes there's some-thing lack-ing what they need's a damn good whack-ing.

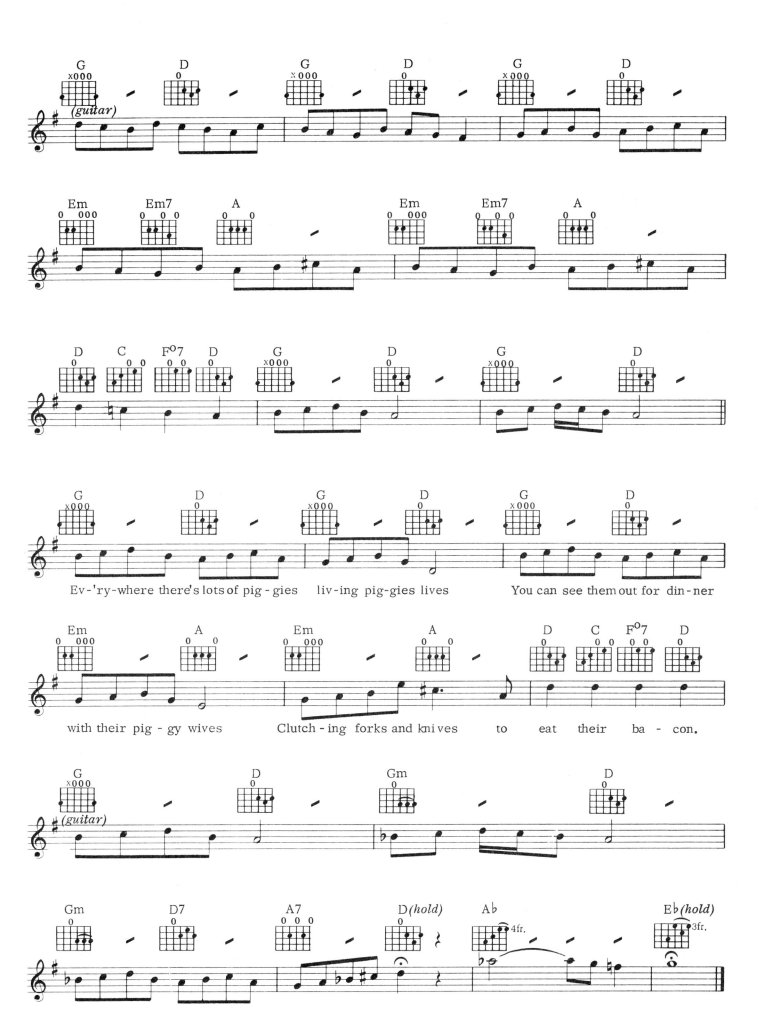

Ev-'ry-where there's lots of pig-gies liv-ing pig-gies lives You can see them out for din-ner

with their pig-gy wives Clutch-ing forks and kni ves to eat their ba - con.

Something

Words and Music: George Harrison

Moderately slow

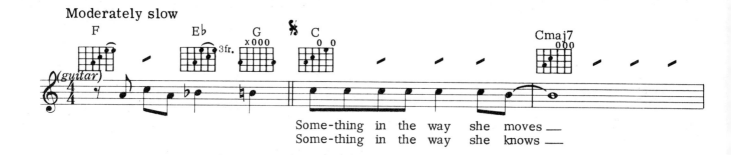

Some-thing in the way she moves ___
Some-thing in the way she knows ___

at-tracts me like no oth-er lov-er. ___
and all I have to do is think of her. ___

Some-thing in the way she
Some-thing in the things she

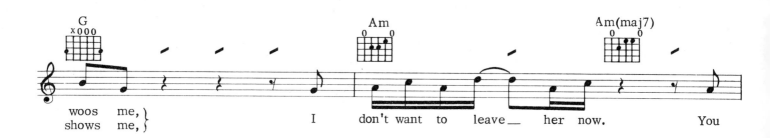

woos me,
shows me, }

I don't want to leave ___ her now. You

To Coda

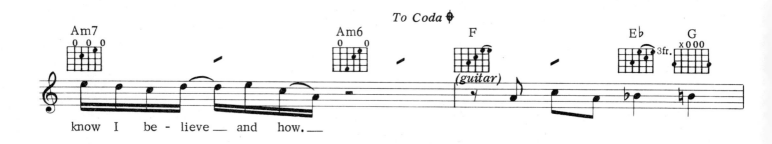

know I be-lieve ___ and how. ___

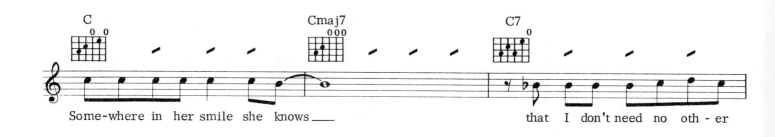

Some-where in her smile she knows ___

that I don't need no oth-er

187

While My Guitar Gently Weeps

Words and Music: George Harrison

189

I Saw Her Standing There

Words and Music: John Lennon & Paul McCartney

2. Well, she looked at me, and I, I could see
   That before too long I'd fall in love with her.
   She wouldn't dance with another,
   Oh, when I saw her standing there.
   Well, my heart went boom *(etc.)*

3. Well, we danced through the night, and we held each other tight,
   And before too long I fell in love with her.
   Now I'll never dance with another,
   Oh, since I saw her standing there.

Monday Morning

Words and Music: Lindsey Buckingham

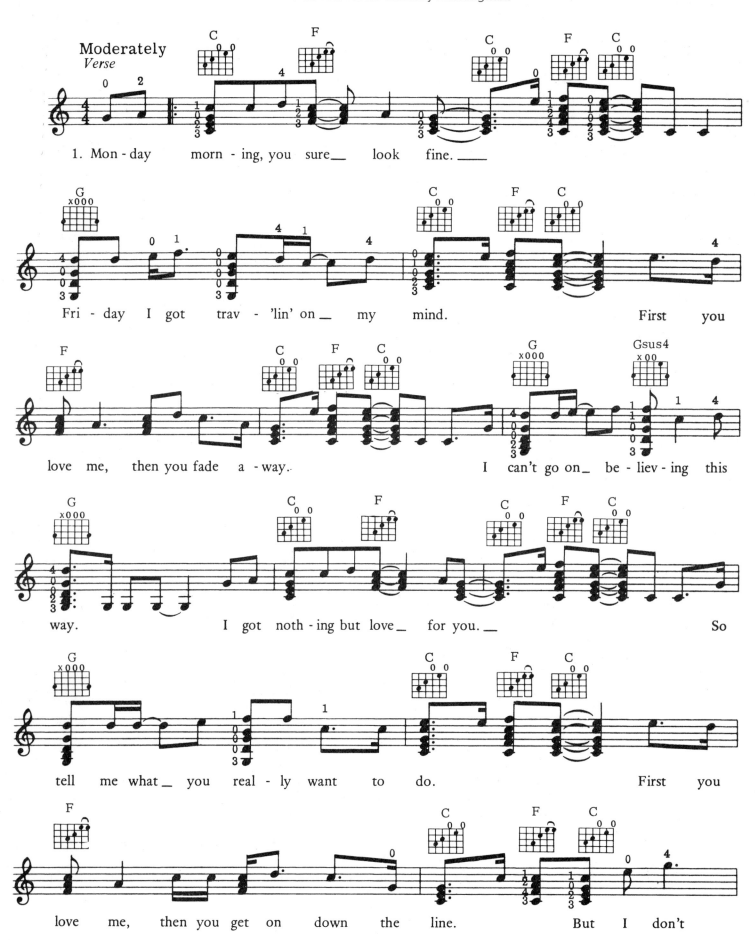

1. Mon - day morn - ing, you sure__ look fine. ___

Fri - day I got trav - 'lin' on __ my mind. First you

love me, then you fade a - way. I can't go on__ be - liev - ing this

way. I got noth - ing but love__ for you. __ So

tell me what__ you real - ly want to do. First you

love me, then you get on down the line. But I don't

Additional lyrics

2. Monday morning, you sure look fine.
   Friday I got travelin' on my mind.
   First you love me, then you say it's wrong.
   You know I can't go on believing for long.
   But you know it's true.
   You only want me when I get over you.
   First you love me, then you get on down the line.
   But I don't mind.
   I don't mind.

Chorus

Second Hand News

Words and Music: Lindsey Buckingham

I'm just sec-ond hand news. I'm just sec-ond hand news.

Additional lyrics

2. One thing I think you should know:
   I ain't gonna miss you when you go.
   Been down so long. I've been tossed around enough.
   Oh, couldn't you just let me go down and do my stuff.
   I know you're hoping to find
   Someone who's gonna give you peace of mind.
   When times go bad, when times go rough,
   Won't you lay me down in the tall grass and let me do my stuff.

Can't Smile Without You

Words and Music: Chris Arnold, David Martin & Geoff Morrow

some peo-ple say___ hap-pi-ness takes___ so ___ ver-y long to find.___

Well, I'm find-ing it hard___ leav-ing your love be-hind___

me. And you see, I can't smile with-out you.
(you.)_____(Instrumental till fade.)

I can't smile with-out you. I can't laugh and I can't sing. I'm

find-ing it hard to do an-y-thing.___ You see I feel glad when

you're glad. I feel sad when you're sad. If you___ on-ly knew what

I'm___ go-ing through: I just can't smile with-out

Tryin' To Get The Feeling Again

Words and Music: David Pomeranz

Iron Maiden

Words and Music: Steve Harris

Won't you come_ in - to_____ my room,_ I wan-na show you

all my wares_ I just want_ to see_____ your blood,_

I just want_ to stand_ and stare._ See the blood_ be - gin_

_ to flow,_ As it falls_ up - on_____ the floor._

(Bridge 1º)

Ir - on Maid - en can't_ be fought,_ Ir - on Maid - en can't_ be sought._

Oh well,— wher - ev - er— wher - ev - er you are.—

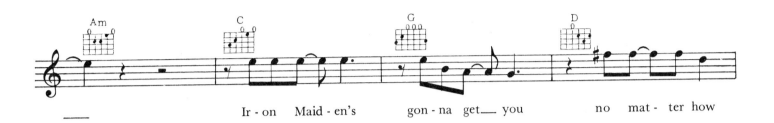

— Ir - on Maid - en's gon - na get— you no mat - ter how

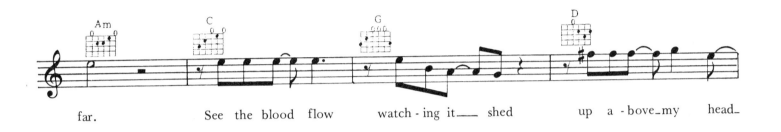

far. See the blood flow watch - ing it— shed up a - bove— my head—

To Coda ⊕

— Ir - on Maid - en wants— you for

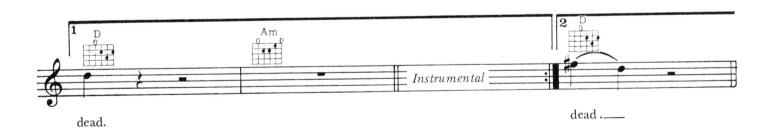

dead. Instrumental dead .—

⊕ CODA

D.C. al Coda   to Fine

Instrumental   Instrumental

dead.————

Sanctuary

Words and Music: Steve Harris, Paul Di'Anno, Dave Murray, Clive Burr, Dennis Straton

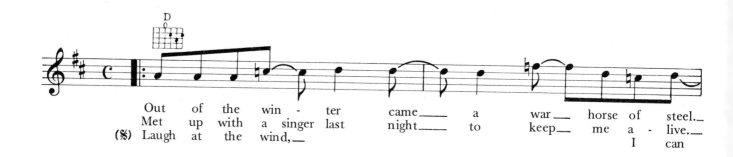

Out of the win - ter came ___ a war ___ horse of steel. ___
Met up with a singer last night ___ to keep ___ me a - live.
(%) Laugh at the wind, ___ I can

___ howl at the rain. ___
I've nev - er killed a wo - man be - fore ___
He spends all his mon - ey on gam-
Down in the can - yon,

___ but I know ___ how it feels. ___
___ bling and guns ___ to sur - vive. ___
or out in the plains. ___

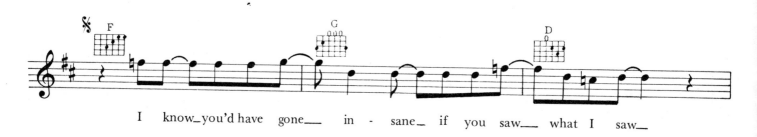

I know ___ you'd have gone ___ in - sane ___ if you saw ___ what I saw ___

so now I've got ___ to look ___ for ___

sanct - uar - y_____ from the law._____

(no rhythm) (add rhythm)

(𝄋) I can

So give me sanc - tu - ar - y from_

_____ the law,_____ and I'll_ be al - right._____ Just give me

sanc - tu - ar - y from_ the law, _____ and love_ me to - night._

To - night._____

To Coda ⊕   D.S. + Repeat verse
al coda
Instrumental

⊕ CODA   to Fine
Instrumental

Ramblin' Man

Words and Music: Forest Richard Betts

Moderately fast

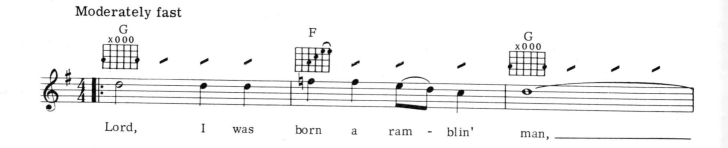

Lord, I was born a ram - blin' man, _____

_____ try'n' to make a liv - in' and do - in' the best I

can. _____ And when it's time for

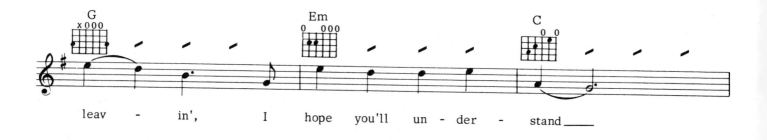

leav - in', I hope you'll un - der - stand ____

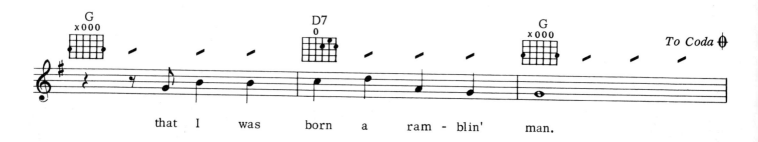

that I was born a ram - blin' man.

Profession Of Violence

Words and Music: Paul Chapman & Phil Mogg

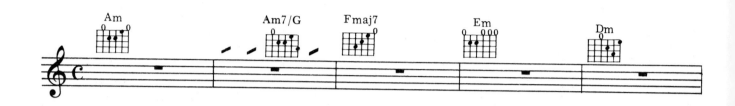

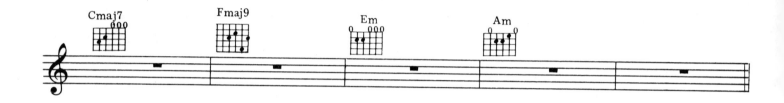

Hey babe what we gon - na do, ___ no look be - hind me glan -
Try to pick up the pie - ces may - be move a - way..

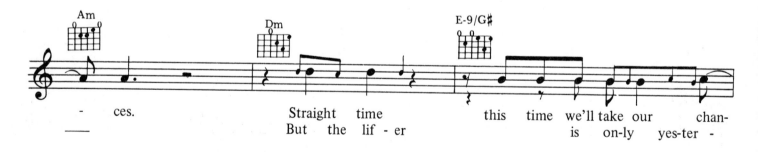

- ces. Straight time this time we'll take our chan -
___ But the lif - er is on - ly yes - ter -

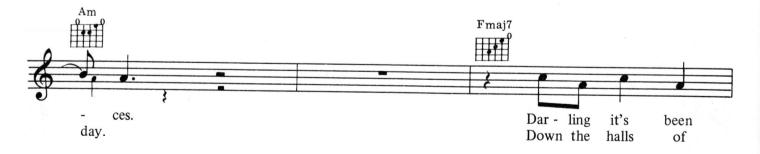

- ces.
day.
Dar - ling it's been
Down the halls of

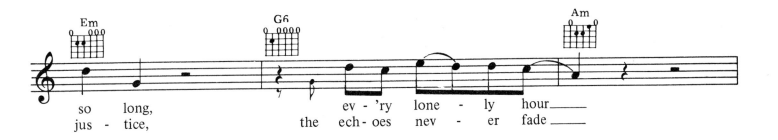

so long, / jus - tice,

ev - 'ry lone - ly hour_____ / the ech - oes nev - er fade _____

Lord, the sin - ner / notch - es on my

pulls the trig - ger and the world_ turns sour. / gun an - oth - er debt is paid..

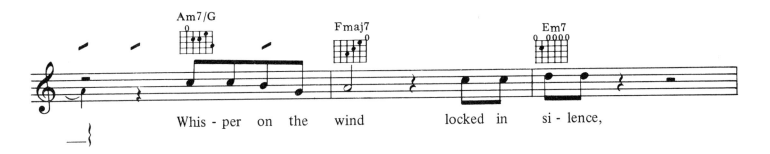

Whis - per on the wind locked in si - lence,

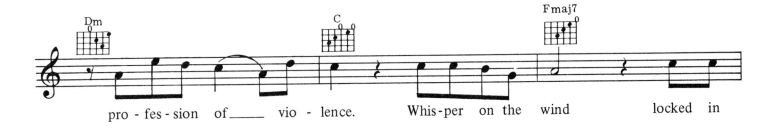

pro - fes - sion of _____ vio - lence. Whis - per on the wind locked in

si - lence pro - fes - sion of _____ vi - o - lence.

Rpt Verse and Chorus
to FINE

(Gtr. solo)

Instr.

207

Lonely Heart

Words and Music: Paul Chapman, Pete Way & Phil Mogg

Sar-ah has her dreams and makes — her plans, — to get what she wants when she can — A lit-tle bit of heav-en was all she asked — for, — in those si-lent mo-ments deep in the night, — she'd find her-self, make it feel al-right — and hun-gers for the bright.

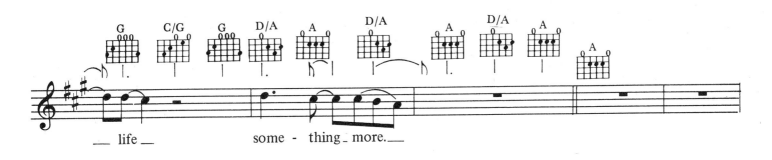

_ life _   some - thing _ more. _

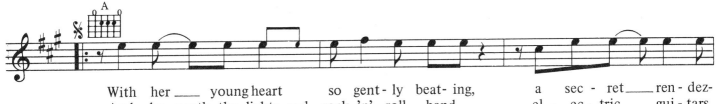

With her _____ young heart   so gent-ly beat-ing,   a sec-ret _____ ren-dez-
And be-neath the lights and rock 'n' roll band,   el-ec-tric _____ gui-tars
And now you cry your-self to sleep,   a-gainst the odds you

vous lov-ers' meet-ing,   out in the night, _   out in the n - n - n - night _
one night stand _ are you   giv-ing a-way, _   giv-ing a-way _ yeah, yeah, yeah _
want-ed to beat   you'll nev-er say no,   nev-er say no, _ no, no, no. _

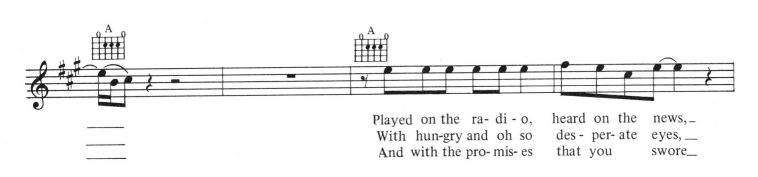

Played on the ra-di-o,   heard on the news, _
With hun-gry and oh so   des-per-ate eyes, _
And with the pro-mis-es   that you   swore _

ba-by's   gone lost, they   found her shoes, _ you can   turn out the light, _ you
the souls who get hurt be-   lieve in their lies, _   you on-ly be-tray, _
the price you pay,   the   love you tore _   now   where did it go, _

Swingtown

Words and Music: Steve Miller & Chris McCarty

Baker Street

Words and Music: Gerry Rafferty

Moderately

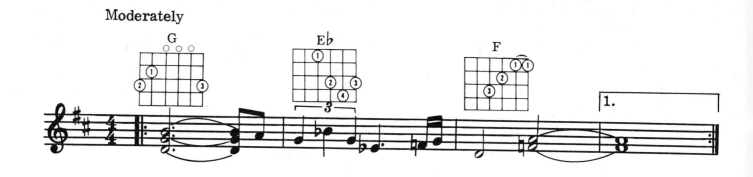

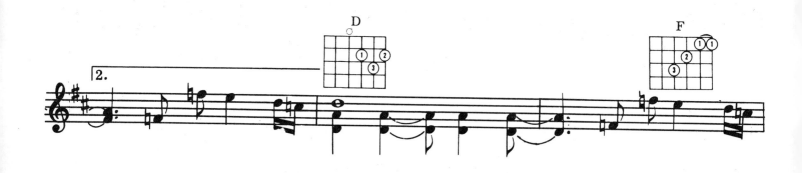

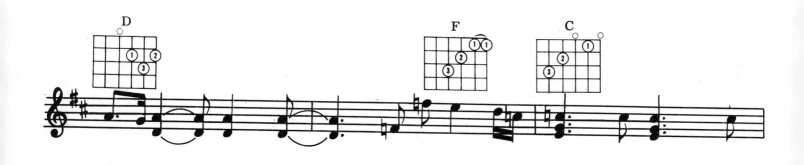

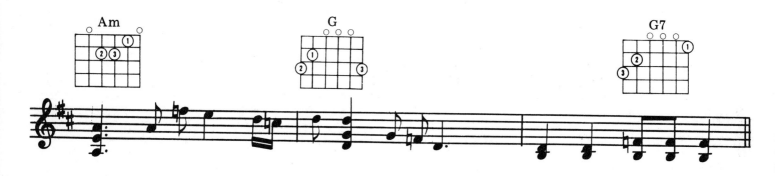

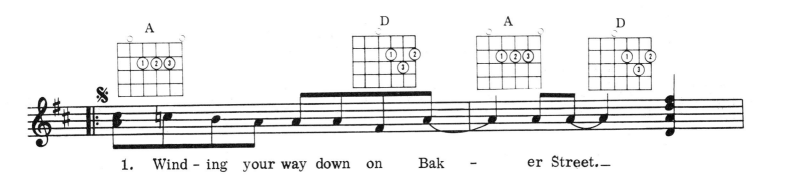

1. Wind - ing your way down on Bak - er Street.—

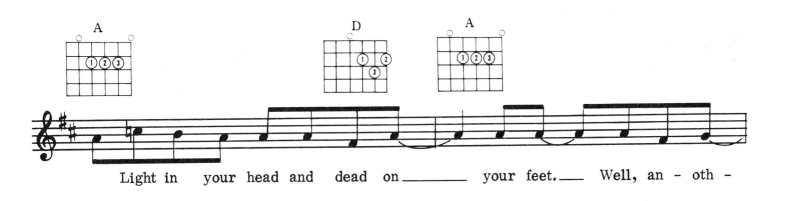

Light in your head and dead on____ your feet.__ Well, an - oth -

er cra - zy day____ you'll drink the night__ a - way__ and for -

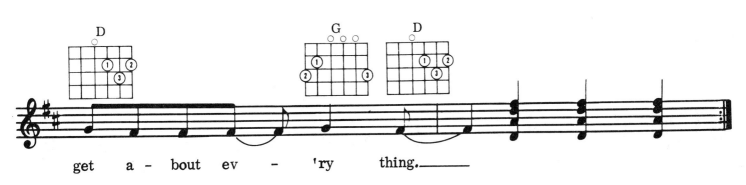

get a - bout ev - 'ry thing._____

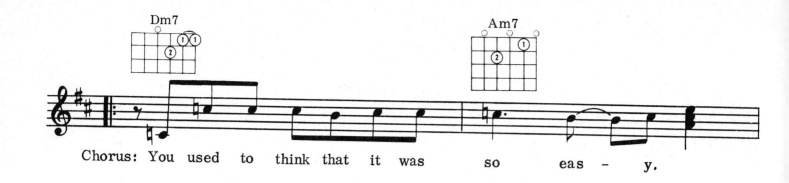

Chorus: You used to think that it was so eas - y.

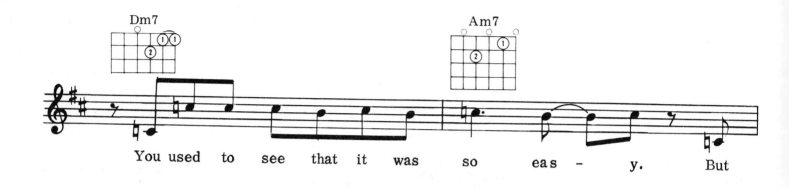

You used to see that it was so eas - y. But

you're try - in', you're try - in' now.____

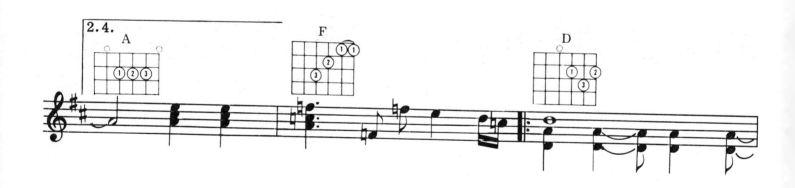

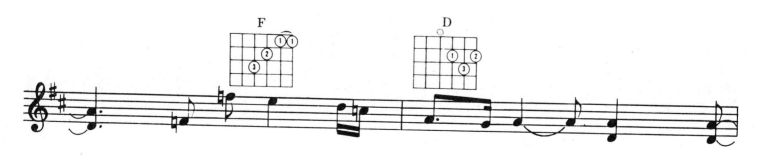

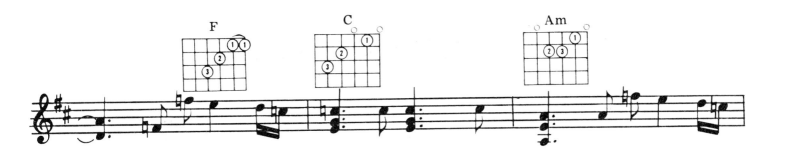

D.S.
2nd time repeat and fade 𝄋

Verse 2:

This city desert makes you feel so cold.

He's got so many people but he's got no soul.

And it's taking so long to find out you were wrong

When you thought it held everything.

Chorus 2:

Another year and then you'll be happy.

Just one more year and then you'll be happy.

But you're cryin', you're cryin' now.

Verse 3:

Way down the street there's a lot in his place,

He opens his door, he's got that look on his face

And he asks you where you've been.

You tell him who you've seen and you talk about anything.

Chorus 3:

But you know you'll always keep movin'.

You know he's never gonna stop movin'.

'Cause he's rollin', he's the rollin' stone.

Verse 4:

He's got this dream about buyin' some land,

He's gonna give up the booze and the one night stands

And then you'll settle down in some quiet little town

And forget about everything.

Chorus 4:

When you wake up it's a new mornin'

The sun is shinin', it's a new mornin'

And you're goin', you're goin' home.

That's The Way (I Like It)

Words and Music: H. W. Casey & R. Finch

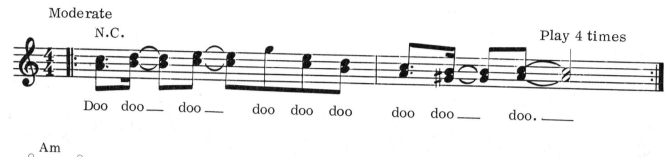

Doo doo — doo — doo doo doo doo doo — doo. —

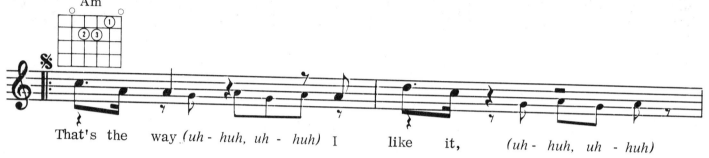

That's the way (uh - huh, uh - huh) I like it, (uh - huh, uh - huh)

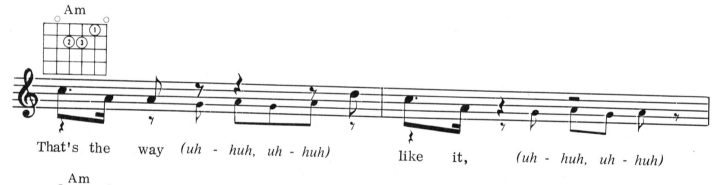

That's the way (uh - huh, uh - huh) like it, (uh - huh, uh - huh)

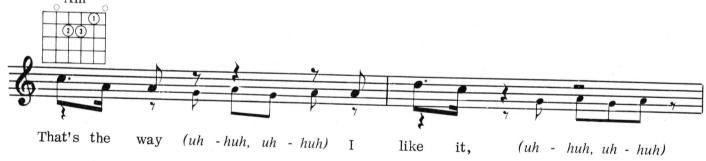

That's the way (uh - huh, uh - huh) I like it, (uh - huh, uh - huh)

That's the way (uh - huh, uh - huh) I like it, (uh - huh, uh - huh)

Dm7

When you take me ____ by the hand, ____ tell me I'm ____ your lov-in'
When I got to ____ be in your arms, ____ when we're all ____ all a-

Dm7

man, when you give ____ me ____ all your love and
lone, when you whis – per ____ sweet in my ear,

1.   2.   D.S. al Coda

do it, babe, ____ the ver-y best you can. Oh,
when you turn, ____ turn me on. Oh,

Coda

Dm7   **Dm7**

say ____ O. K. *(uh - huh)* That's the way *(uh-huh)* that's the way *(uh - huh)*

Am

That's the way *(uh - huh, uh - huh)* I like it, *(uh - huh, uh - huh)*

Repeat and Fade ad lib.

That's the way *(uh - huh, uh - huh)* I like it, *(uh - huh, uh - huh)*

217

Lido Shuffle

Words and Music: Boz Scaggs & David Paich

The Letter
Words and Music: Wayne Carson Thompson

ba - by just wrote_ me a let - ter._____ Well she

wrote me a let - ter said she could-n't live_ with-out me no more.__

Lis - ten mis - ter can't you see I got to get back_ to my

ba - by once more,_ An - y-way. Give me a tick -et for an air - plane,

Ain't got time_ to take the fast-est train. Lone-ly days are gone,_

I'm a - go-in' home, My ba - by just wrote me a let-ter._____ Well she

Repeat for fade

let - ter._ My ba - by just wrote_ me a let - ter._ My

221

Let's Twist Again

Words and Music: Kal Mann & Dave Appell

Moderately

Let's   Twist   A - gain, ___   like we did   last   sum - mer. _____

Yeah,   Let's   Twist   A - gain, ___   like we did   last   year. __

_____   Don't - cha   re - mem - ber   when

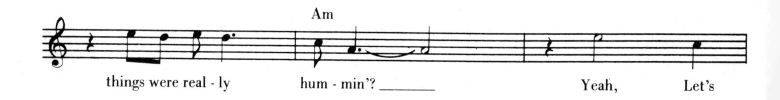

things were real - ly   hum - min'? _____   Yeah,   Let's

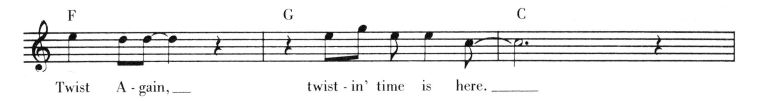

F   G   C

Twist   A - gain, ___   twist - in'   time   is   here. _____

C7   F

Ee - ah   'roun'   'n   a   'roun'   'n   a   up   'n   down   we

C   F

go_____ a -   gain.   Oh   ba - by,   make   me   know   you   love   me

G7

so,_____ an' _____ then   Let's   Twist   A - gain, ___

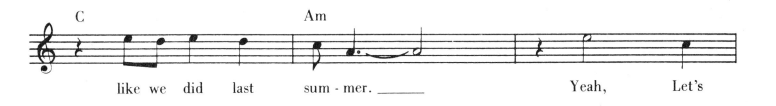

C   Am

like   we   did   last   sum - mer. _____   Yeah,   Let's

F   G   C

Twist   A - gain, ___   like   we   did   last   year. _____

Tobacco Road

Words and Music: John D. Loudermilk

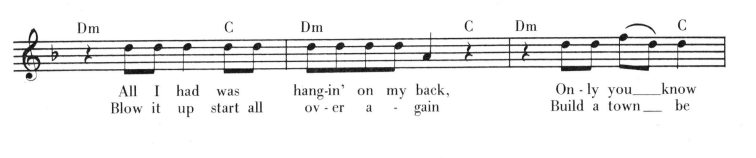

All I had was   hang-in' on my back,   On - ly you___know
Blow it up start all   ov - er a - gain   Build a town__ be

how I loathe ___   This place called   To - bac - co Road _____
proud to show ___   Give the name __   To - bac - co Road _____

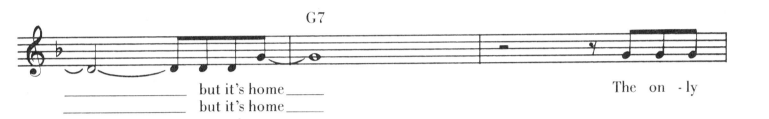

_____ but it's home_____   The on - ly
_____ but it's home_____

life I've___ ev - er known   On - ly you ___
    I des - pise __

_____ know how I loathe _____   But I love __
_____ you 'cos you're filth - y ___

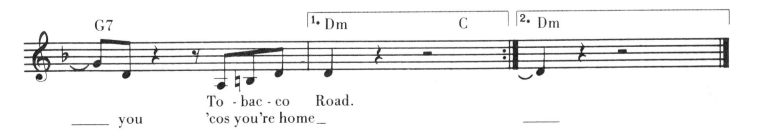

    To - bac - co Road.
_____ you   'cos you're home _   _____

Chuck E's In Love

Words and Music: Rickie Lee Jones

Escape (The Pina Colada Song)

Words and Music: Rupert Holmes

Additional lyrics

2. I didn't think about my lady;
   I know that sounds kind of mean.
   But me and my old lady
   Have fallen into the same old dull routine.
   So I wrote to the paper,
   Took out a personal ad.
   And though I'm nobody's poet,
   I thought it wasn't half bad:
   "Yes, I like piña coladas
   And getting caught in the rain.
   I'm not much into health food;
   I am into champagne.
   I've got to meet you by tomorrow noon,
   And cut through all this red tape,
   At a bar called O'Malley's
   Where we'll plan our escape."

3. So I waited with high hopes
   And she walked in the place.
   I knew her smile in an instant.
   I knew the curve of her face.
   It was my lovely lady
   And she said, " Oh,it's you. "
   Then we laughed for a moment
   And I said, " I never knew
   That you like piña coladas,
   Getting caught in the rain,
   And the feel of the ocean
   And the taste of champagne.
   If you'd like making love at midnight
   In the dunes on the Cape,
   You're the lady I've looked for.
   Come with me and escape."

You Make Me Feel Like Dancing

Words and Music: Leo Sayer & Vincent Poncia

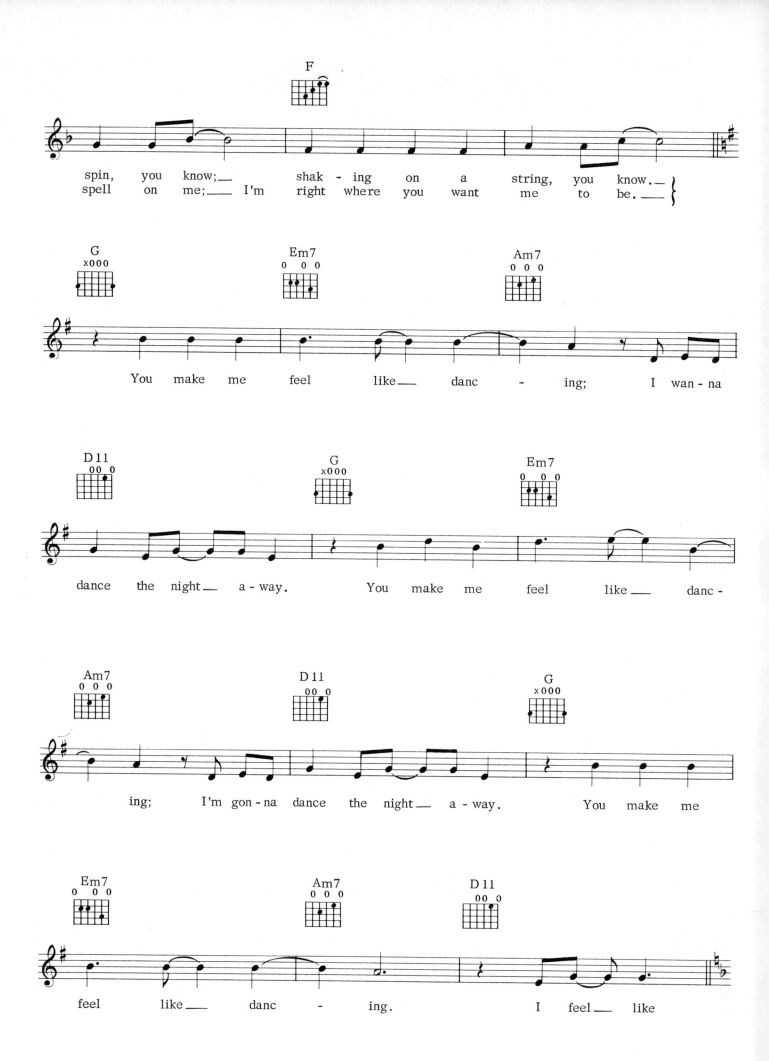

Time Passages
Words & Music: Al Stewart & Peter White

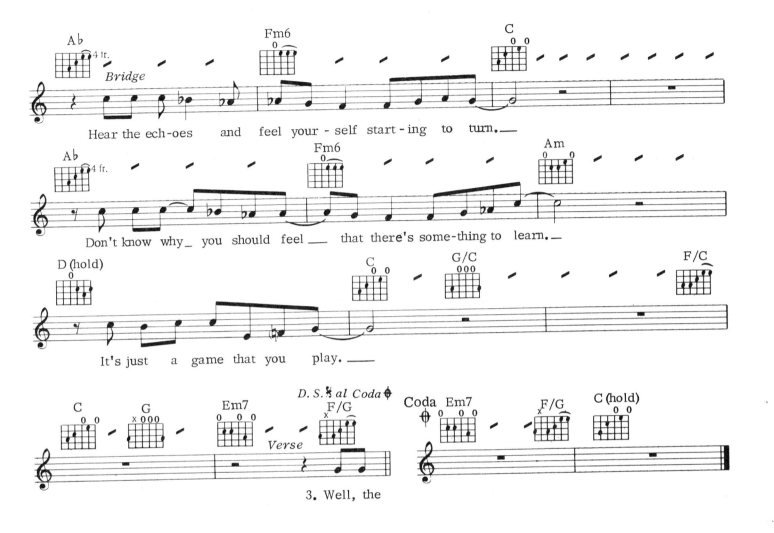

Bridge

Hear the ech-oes   and feel your - self start - ing to turn. —

Don't know why_ you should feel __ that there's some-thing to learn. —

It's just   a game that you   play. —

D.S. % al Coda

Verse

3. Well, the

Coda

Additional lyrics

2. Well, I'm not the kind to live in the past.
   The years run too short and the days too fast.
   The things you lean on are things that don't last.
   Well, it's just now and then my line gets cast into these
   Time passages.
   There's something back there that you left behind.
   Oh, time passages.
   Buy me a ticket on the last train home tonight.

(Bridge)

3. Well, the picture is changing, now you're part of a crowd.
   They're laughing at something, the music's loud.
   A girl comes toward you, you once used to know.
   You reach out your hand, but you're all alone in those
   Time passages.
   I know you're in there; you're just out of sight.
   Oh, time passages.
   Buy me a ticket on the last train home tonight.

Hey Hey, My My (Into The Black)

Words and Music: Neil Young

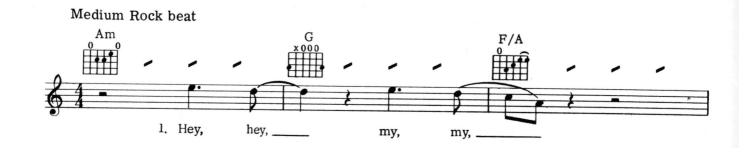

1. Hey, hey, _____ my, my, _____

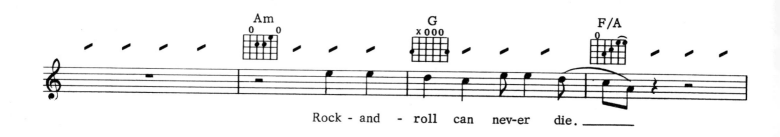

Rock - and - roll can nev-er die. _____

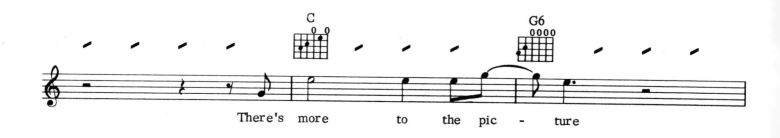

There's more to the pic - ture

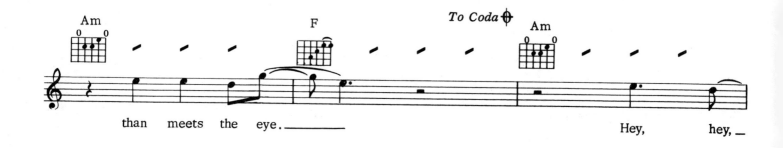

than meets the eye. _____ Hey, hey, _

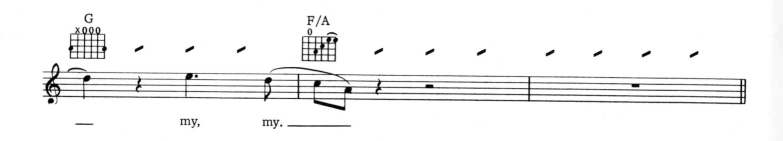

_ my, my. _____

The Loner

Words and Music: Neil Young

Additional lyrics

2. If you see him in the subway, he'll be down at the end of the car,
Watching you move until he knows he knows who you are.
When you get off at your station alone, he'll know that you are.

(Chorus)

3. There was a woman he knew about a year or so ago.
She had something that he needed and he pleaded with her not to go.
On the day that she left, he died, but it did not show.

(Chorus)

Ohio

Words and Music: Neil Young

Moderate March tempo

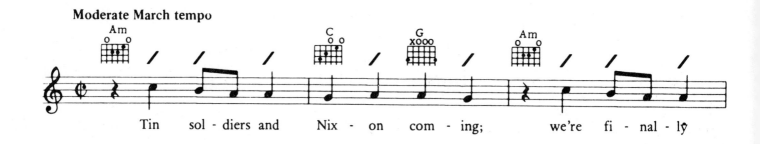

Tin sol-diers and Nix-on com-ing; we're fi-nal-ly

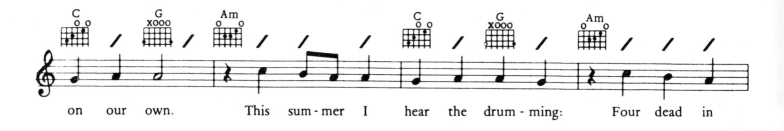

on our own. This sum-mer I hear the drum-ming: Four dead in

To Coda

O - hi - o. Gotta get down to it, sol-diers are
What if you knew her and found _ her

gun-ning us down; should-a been done long a - go.
dead on the ground; how can you run when you know?

Repeat and fade

Four dead in O - hi - o.

The Needle And The Damage Done

Words and Music: Neil Young

Ring My Bell

Words and Music: Frederick Knight

*optional

Stairway To Heaven

Words and Music: Jimmy Page & Robert Plant

There's a la-dy who's sure all that glit-ters is gold_ and she's
sign on the wall but she wants to be sure,_ 'cause you

buy-ing a stair-way to heav-en. When she gets there she knows if the
know some-times words have two mean-ings. In a tree by the brook there's a

stores are all closed_ with a word she can get what she came_ for. There's a
song-bird who sings;_ some-times all of our thoughts are mis-

giv - en.   Oo, _____ it makes me won-der.

There's a

feel - ing I get   when I   look   to the   west___   and my
whis - pered that soon,   if we   all   call the   tune,___   then the

spir - it is cry - ing for leav - ing.   In my
pip - er will lead us to rea - son.   And a

thoughts I have seen   rings of   smoke through the   trees___   and the
new day will dawn   for___   those who stand   long___   and the

voic - es of those who stand look - ing.   And it's
for - ests will ech - o with   laugh - ter.

The books below are available from your local music shop
who will order them for you if not in stock.
If there is no music shop near you, you may order direct from
Music Sales Limited (Dept. M), 8/9 Frith Street, London W1V 5TZ.
Please always include £1 to cover post/packing costs.

Play Country Blues Guitar
Stefan Grossman

A thorough insight into
blues guitar and
techniques and a study of
the art of great bluesmen.
Delta, ragtime and bottle-
neck in standard notation
and tablature.

64 pages, AM 25833

Play Country Style Guitar
Chris Spedding

Easy-to-follow instruction.
Chord diagrams for all
accompaniments and an
index of 'country &
western' chords in diagram
form and musical notation.

30 pages, CL 10059

Play Ragtime Guitar
Stefan Grossman

The styles and techniques
of ragtime guitar and every
aspect of it from ragtime
folk to classic rags in
ordinary notation and
tablature.

96 pages, AM 35285

Private Guitar Lessons
Bob Baxter

In this book with record
series Bob Baxter instructs
you as he would in your
own home in all types of
playing.

Book 1 48 pages, AM 35688
Book 2 48 pages, AM 35676
Book 3 48 pages, AM 35684

Django Reinhardt
Stan Ayeroff

Sixteen solos as played by
the legendary guitarist.
With chord changes,
analysis of the style and an
extensive discography.
Jazz Masters Series

70 pages, AM 23235

**Richard Lieberson's Old-
Time Fiddle Tunes for
Guitar**

Forty tunes for the flat-
picker with notes on
playing back-up and
special effects. Standard
notation and tablature.
Discography and
bibliography.

128 pages, AM 16585

The Lee Ritenour Book

Eight solos edited and
transcribed by Rich
Carter. Plus performance
notes by Lee Ritenour—
guitarist, composer,
arranger.

60 pages, AM 31105

Rhythm Guitar
Harvey Vinson

Rhythm and back-up
playing, how to form a
band, chords and records
you should know—in fact
everything needed to teach
yourself.

128 pages, AM 10687

Rock Chord Guide
Harvey Vinson

An important guide to lead
or rhythm guitar, the
chords and styles
demonstrated teach you to
play in any key and in any
position. Profusely
illustrated.

112 pages, AM 10612

**Rock 'n' Roll Guitar
Case Chord Book**
Russ Shipton

Best reference book ever
for the rock 'n' roll
guitarist. Fits into the
guitar case.

48 pages, AM 28689

**Rock Picture Chords and
How to Use Them**
Mark Michaels

The most often used chord,
progressions and right
hand patterns in clear
diagrams and photos with
tunes to play.

30 pages, AM 21718

Rock Riffs for Bass
Tom Wolk

Indispensable to the
musician who needs a
repertory of authentic rock
styles—a catalogue of
ideas.

46 pages, AM 23508

B.B. King

Articles, music, lyrics,
photos and quotes from the
great performer. The songs
are written in standard
music notation and guitar
tablature, plus chords.
Illustrated.

64 pages, AM 10679

Latin American

Thirty-eight Latin
American songs arranged
for easy guitar with lyrics,
chord symbols and guitar
boxes.

80 pages, AM 14440

Lead Guitar
Harvey Vinson

Basic styles of rock guitar—
improvisation, blues, riffs
etc. Plus a record for
tuning and R & B
background.

112 pages, AM 11198

Learn Dobro Techniques
Stephen Toth

Bluegrass and Country
music the way it should be
played—this book takes
you from basics through to
endings.

60 pages, AM 17344

**Mickey Baker's Jazz and
Rhythm Blues**

Technical exercises, tips
on practising, and the
Mickey Baker style
illustrated by examples
written by famous Jazz and
Rhythm 'n' Blues musicians.

64 pages, CL 10174

**Mickey Baker's Jazz
Guitar**

Teaches the playing of
chords the modern way,
vamps and fill-ins, bop
blues, bounce blues,
theory, technique, etc.

72 pages, CL 10158

**Advanced Picture Chords
for Guitar**
Russ Shipton
A key by key guide to
chord triads, chord
substitutes, moveable
chord shapes and useful
chord sequences. Clearly
illustrated with photos and
diagrams.

32 pages. AM 25040

**Basic Guitar Scale
Manual**
Harvey Vinson
Scales, exercises, rock and
blues progressions for all
grades in all the important
keys. Standard notation
and tablature, plus full-
colour note-finder poster.

144 pages. AM 14796

Bass Guitar
Jim Gregory & Harvey
Vinson
Basics, plus blues
progressions, walking bass
lines etc. With scores of
riffs to practise and
instruction record.

78 pages. AM 14028

**Arnie Berle's Complete
Handbook for Jazz
Improvisation**
A practical guide to the
development of jazz
technique for guitar,
piano, wind and all treble
clef instruments.

72 pages. AM 26626

**Bluegrass Picture Chords
and How to Use Them**
Happy Traum
The most-often used
chords, progressions and
right hand patterns in clear
diagrams and photographs
plus tunes to practise.

32 pages. AM 21684

**Blues Picture Chords and
How to Use Them**
Happy Traum
Clear diagrams and photos
of the most-often used right
hand patterns, plus blues
tunes for practise.

32 pages. AM 21676

Blues Riffs For Guitar
by Mark Michaels
This book takes in riffs and
patterns in the styles of the
modern bluesmen and the
city blues singers like
Freddie King, B.B. King,
Buddy Guy and Otis Rush.
A compendium and
source- book with chord
changes, notes,
performing hints and a
discography.

48 pages. AM 24613

**Chords for Rhythm
Guitar**
Eric Kershaw
Every dance band chord
for guitar shown in both
diagram form and musical
notation. Fingering is also
shown.

44 pages. CL 10042

Charlie Christian
Stan Ayeroff
Eighteen solos as played
by the pioneer of jazz
guitar. With chord
changes, an analysis of the
style, plus a complete
discography.
Jazz Masters Series

70 pages. AM 24316

**The Complete Guitar
Player Chord Book**
Russ Shipton
Shows exactly what chords
are needed to both play
and arrange songs. Many
clear photographs plus
unique demonstration
record.

16 pages. AM 31717

**The Complete Guitar
Player Songbook**
Contains all the songs and
music featured in The
Complete Guitar Player.
In standard notation with
diagrams and chord
symbols plus full lyrics.

40 pages. AM 26527

**The Complete Guitar
Player Songbook No. 2**
This new book contains 50
songs which are arranged
in keys which are
examined in 'The
Complete Guitar Player'
books. Includes chords,
left hand fingerings and
right hand rhythm pattern,
also lyrics.

48 pages. AM 31634

**The Complete Guitar
Player Songbook No. 3**
Another 50 songs by Paul
McCartney, The Rolling
Stones, Buddy Holly etc.
Russ Shipton arrangements
in standard notation with
chord boxes and full lyrics.
Useful references to The
Complete Guitar Course
are printed with each
song.

48 pages. AM 33291

**The Complete Guitar
Player Songbook No. 4**
The latest in this series, all
of which are of special
interest to players who
have followed The
Complete Guitar Player
Course. 50 songs by Billy
Joel, John Denver, Elvis
Presley etc. In standard
notation with chord boxes
and full lyrics.

48 pages. AM 33754

**The Complete Guitar
Player**
Russ Shipton
For classroom or private
use. Easy to follow text with
diagrams and
demonstration
photographs. Special
bands of colour focus the
attention of the guitarist on
the music. All songs or
solos are on one page or
facing pages. Most of the

course is based on the
music of modern
performers such as Bob
Dylan, John Denver and
the Beatles. Enables you to
play right from lesson one
to an advanced stage, and,
assumes you have no
knowledge of music.

Book 1 32 pages. AM 25123
Also contains pull-out chord chart
and unique tuning record.
Book 2 32 pages. AM 25131
Book 3 32 pages. AM 25149
Book 4 32 pages. AM 25156

Omnibus Edition Books 1, 2, 3 and
4 AM 26691
Complete Set of separate books
also available. AM 25164

Cassettes
A cassette has been
produced for each book to
supplement the tuition. All
the guitar solos featured in
the books are played by
Russ Shipton and in
addition he plays and sings
all the songs therein.

Rock Riffs for Guitar
Mark Michaels

Authentic rock phrases for soloing, riffs and patterns in the styles of Chuck Berry, Jeff Beck etc. Plus chord changes, performing hints and a discography.

28 pages. AM 22211

Shirley Douglas' Easy Guide to Rhythm & Blues for Bass Guitar

A complete course progresses from scales and exercises to bass guitar, riffs. Fingering charts, diagrams and professional short cuts.

40 pages. AM 11073

Step-by-Step Rock Guitar
Happy & Artie Traum

Instruction in electric blues guitar, transcriptions of B.B. King's solos in music notation and tablature plus guide to, and history and analysis of rhythm and lead guitar. Illustrated.

126 pages. AM 11008

Steve Howe Guitar Pieces

Original Steve Howe guitar solos with performance notes from Steve—and Mick Barker, who transcribed them. Includes 'Clap', 'Sound Chaser' and 'Ram'.

48 pages. AM 26345

Teach Yourself Bluegrass Bass
by Roger Mason

Clear instruction from a professional. Basics, solos, back-up, right and left hand techniques and personal advice on performance. Plus a selection of the best bluegrass tunes and songs.

48 pages. AM 21601

Teach Yourself Bluegrass Guitar
Russ Barenberg

Basic techniques, solos, back-ups, performance advice etc. plus bluegrass melodies and a discography are in this book written by a professional.

63 pages. AM 21627

The Improviser's Bass Method
Chuck Sher

For beginner to professional. Includes transcribed bass lines and solos. Spiral bound.

218 pages. AM 30636

Improvising Jazz Bass
Richard Laird

Tunes and exercises in the styles of Eddie Gomez, Ron Carter etc. Plus professional insights into jazz scales, rhythms, equipment etc. Bibliography and discography.

112 pages. AM 27939

Improvising Rock Guitar
by Artie Traum and Arti Funaro

Based on the playing styles of Eric Clapton, Jimi Hendrix, Chuck Berry and other famous guitarists. Includes lead and rhythm guitar techniques for improvising rock 'n' roll and other modern styles. In standard notation and tablature.

94 pages. AM 32012

Jazz and Popular Songs arranged for Classical Guitar

John Duarte's arrangements of music for the classical guitar — the melodies of Lennon & McCartney, Duke Ellington, Burt Bacharach and other modern composers.

AY 15422

Ivor Mairant's Graduated Guitar Course

For playing all forms of popular music. Instead of scales and exercises a melodic approach is adopted.

Book 1 32 pages, SM 04754
Book 2 32 pages, SM 04762
Book 3 32 pages, SM 10983
Book 4 32 pages, SM 04754

Jazz Chords for Guitar
Richard Boukas

Over 600 jazz chord voicings illustrated by a new chordgraph system. Special theory section also included.

40 pages. AM 22070

Jazz Guitar Chord Bible
Warren Nunes

The complete guide to three and four string chords by a world-acclaimed guitar teacher. Over 400 chords and complete grid diagram of each one.

Vol. 1. 120 pages. AM 25792
Vol. 2. 72 pages. AM 33366

Jazz Picture Chords and How to Use Them
Artie Traum

The most often used chords, progressions and right hand patterns in clear diagrams and photos, plus tunes to play.

32 pages. AM 21700

Jazz Riffs for Bass
Rick Laird

A repertory of ideas for playing modal jazz, jazz fusion and blues. Riffs and patterns in the styles of Eddie Gomez etc. plus tunes to play.

48 pages. AM 24605

Jazz Riffs for Guitar
Richard Boukas

Authentic jazz phrases for soloing, plus riffs and patterns in the styles of Wes Montgomery, George Benson and others. Plus solos to play.

32 pages. AM 23565

J.J. Cale: Guitar Styles

Photographs and comments on each of the 21 songs provide an insight into the artist's technical and creative talent.

84 pages. AM 27624

The Joy of Guitar
Happy Traum

Easy arrangements of folk, popular and standard songs in a progressive chord-by-chord manner with simple instruction.

80 pages. YK 21079.

The Baroque Guitar

The solos, duets and songs are from the original sources and are graded and fingered. With introductory text and study notes. By de Visée, Sanz and master composers for the lute. See also *The Classical Guitar* and *The Renaissance Guitar*.

127 pages. AM 35890

The Beatles for Classical Guitar

Beatles numbers arranged by Joe Washington complete with right and left hand fingering. Plus hints on classical guitar technique and performance of these solos.

Book 1 86 pages, 20 solos. NO 17444
Book 2 36 pages, 11 solos. NO 17782

The Classic Guitar Collection Vol. 1

Solos for classical guitar from the fourteenth century to Bartok, including works by Carcassi, Sor and Giuliani.

96 pages. AY 15265

The Classic Guitar Collection Vol. 2

A unique compilation of short pieces for the classical guitar, from the fourteenth century to Shostakovitch and Stravinsky.

126 pages. AY 15273

The Classic Guitar Collection Vol. 3

Outstanding music for guitar players of all standards, edited by Leonid Bolotine and including works by Bach, Mozart and Sor.

96 pages. AY 15281

The Classical Guitar

The solos, duets and songs are from the original sources and are graded and fingered. By Sor, Giuliani and other guitar masters from the early 19th Century. See also *The Baroque Guitar* and *The Renaissance Guitar*.

144 pages. AM 35908

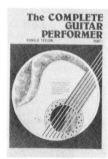

The Complete Guitar Performer, Part I
Ronald Taylor

A progressive course of lessons formulated to encourage correct technique in all aspects of guitar playing in the classic manner. Illustrated with diagrams.

42 pages. RY 20010

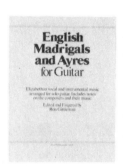

English Madrigals and Ayres for Guitar
Edited and Fingered by Ron Gittleman

Elizabethan vocal and instrumental music for solo guitar. Includes notes on the composers and their music.

32 pages. AY 15307

Flamenco Guitar
Manitas de Plata

Extended excerpts from the recorded solos of Manitas de Plata with examples of the vocal stylizations of José Reyes.

32 pages. AM 24506

Flute and Guitar Duets

Book 1 Beginners. Book 2 Intermediate. Flute part may be used by a violinist. Book 1 is suitable for recorder. 16 pages.

Christmas Carols
Book 1 UM 10007
Book 2 UM 10015
Popular Folk Songs
Book 1 UM 10023
Book 2 UM 10031

The Guitar Songbook

Traditional songs; negro spirituals; melodies of Beethoven, Purcell etc; seventy-two in all in solo and duet arrangement. Plus an illustrated review of guitar technique and reading.

160 pages. AM 10562

G. F. Handel
Selected Solos and Duets

16 pages. AY 15109

The Irish Collection

Fourteen Irish pieces arranged for guitar by John Loesberg.

Vol. 1 Easy/Intermediate
20 pages, BX 54422
Vol. 2 More advanced
20 pages, BX 54430

Laurindo Almeida Contemporary Moods for Classical Guitar

Basic guitar instruction plus twenty-two unique arrangements of tunes including 'Deep Purple', 'The Shadow of Your Smile' and the theme from 'Zorba the Greek'.

61 pages. UA 00731

Matteo Carcassi
Three Sonatinas, Opus 1,

36 pages. AY 15091

Mauro Giuliani
Sonata in C Major, Opus 15

40 pages. AY 15117

Mauro Giuliani
Grand Duo Concertante Opus 85

A revised version of the original edition, also an introduction with historical and performance notes.

36 pages. AY 15232

Playing the Guitar

An illustrated self-instructor, with an introduction to song accompaniment, solo playing and flamenco.

145 pages. AM 10521